RABBIT KEEPING

THIS is a handy, practical guide for all who keep, or intend to keep, rabbits for meat and fur.

It is full of sensible advice on the care, breeding and management, etc., and answers the essential questions raised by rabbit keepers on how to get the maximum profit from their hobby.

RABBIT KEEPING

BY
C. F. SNOW

W. & G. FOYLE LTD·
119–125 CHARING CROSS ROAD
LONDON, W.C.2

First Published 1951
Reprinted August 1952
Revised Edition October 1955
Reprinted October 1958
Reprinted December 1959
Reprinted March 1962
Reprinted November 1962
Reprinted September 1964
Reprinted April 1966
Reprinted April 1968
Reprinted June 1969
Reprinted August 1970
Revised Edition 1974

This edition typeset in 10pt Times

Photoset, printed and bound
in Great Britain by
REDWOOD   BURN   LIMITED
Trowbridge & Esher.

CONTENTS

INTRODUCTION

THE breeding of tame rabbits is no new thing in this country. For more than half a century it has been an absorbing, and in many cases, profitable hobby for a great number of people. During the last ten years, owing to the continued shortage of meat, the number of rabbit-breeders has increased enormously, but there is still a need for many more. The tame rabbit is one of the nation's most important domestic animals, for no other animal of comparable size can produce so much meat in so short a time. The rabbit actually produces more meat in a year than a sheep, and at less cost.

In addition to the speed with which it reproduces itself, the tame rabbit can be housed in a very small space. Even town dwellers with only a small backyard can accommodate a few rabbits. Well-kept rabbits are quite unobjectionable to their owners, and will not give offence to even the most particular of neighbours.

Rabbits are cleanly, hardy animals and suffer from very few ailments. They will thrive in outdoor hutches, if they are protected from winds and driving rain, quite as well as in hutches under cover.

The great advantage the tame rabbit has over other meat-producing animals is that it can be kept almost entirely on household waste. It will thrive on peelings, fish waste, plate-scrapings, and all the waste from green vegetables used in the kitchen. For a large part of the year wild greenfood can form a big part of its diet, and these wild greens can also be dried for winter feeding. Every year thousands of tons of wild greens, which could be turned into valuable rabbit meat, are allowed to go to waste all over the country.

There has always been a big demand for rabbit meat in this country, and a great many rabbits are imported every year. Before the war, 8,000 tons of rabbit flesh was imported annually from the Dominions and the Continent, in addition to the rabbits produced in this country. This, more than anything else, testifies to the goodness of rabbit meat, which is richer in protein than beef, and has almost as high a protein value as chicken, which it closely resembles in appearance and flavour. The flesh of a rabbit of normal size contains the nutritive value of four-and-a-half pounds of beef, shoulder of mutton, or pork.

In addition to the meat it produces, the rabbit also provides a most useful pelt. The modern fur varieties, such as the Beveren, Chinchilla, Havana and the Rex varieties provide pelts which will make up into beautiful coats, capes, or gloves, of which the wearer can be justly proud. One variety, the Angora, grows wool which can be spun and knitted up into garments which cannot be beaten for lightness, warmth and luxurious appearance.

It can be seen, therefore, that the tame rabbit has much to recommend it, and few difficulties in management or breeding which even the novice cannot quickly and easily overcome.

CHAPTER 1

BREEDS OF RABBITS

THE newcomer to rabbit-breeding will find that he has a very varied range of rabbits from which to make his selection. People often ask which is the best rabbit for meat or for meat and fur production. The answer is, of course, that no particular breed of rabbit can claim to be the best for producing meat or pelts. The only rabbit which is best for its particular purpose is the wool-producing Angora, the only rabbit with a woolly coat.

Rabbits can be divided into four groups:

1. *Pelt and Carcase Producers.*—These are the breeds that carry a valuable pelt and are classified as fur rabbits.

2. *Fancy Varieties.*—These are rabbits with specified markings or characteristics. They produce good carcases, but the pelts are not of such commercial value as those of the fur breeds.

3. *Cross-bred Rabbits.*—These are usually produced by mating two different pure breeds together. The result should be hardy, quick-growing youngsters, ideal for table purposes.

4. *The Wool-bearing Angora* which also provides a good carcase. As it is not necessary to kill Angoras to obtain their wool, these are not so suitable for carcase production as the other varieties.

First let us deal with the fur breeds.

Argentès

These can be had in four colours: *Argentè de Champagne*—bluish white and black coat, giving the appearance of old silver, with a dark slate-blue under-colour. A big rabbit, weighing from eight to ten pounds.

Argentè Bleu: Coat bluish-silver with lavender-blue

under-colour   A   smaller   rabbit   than   the   champagne, weighing only about six pounds.

Argentè Crème: An orange-tinted cream-coloured rabbit, weighing about five pounds.

Argentè Brun: The latest addition to the Argentè family, brownish-white in colour, with deep brown under-colour. Weight six pounds.

These rabbits originated in France, and the Argentè de Champagne is named after the French province of its origin. They have well-fleshed limbs, and make excellent table rabbits. The average size of a litter is from five to six.

Beveren: The Beveren can also be obtained in four colours: blue, black, white and brown. The blue is the most popular colour of the four and should be a clear shade of lavender-blue. The blacks should be jet-black and show no rusty tinge; the white should be a clear white, free from creaminess, and the browns a good nut-brown colour.

The Beveren is a big rabbit, weighing over seven pounds, and is an excellent breed for meat and fur. It is hardy and grows well and the pelts are easy to match up.

Beverens were bred at Beveren, near Antwerp, as long ago as 1898, but the breed became popular in this country during the 1914–18 war, owing to its excellence as a meat producer. The pelt in those days was appreciated very little. Since then the pelt has been very much improved, and the Beveren now ranks as one of our best normal-coated fur rabbits.

There are usually six or more youngsters in a litter of Beverens.

Beaver: This is a big rabbit, with a brown coat resembling that of the real beaver, and with a bluish-grey under-colour. It weighs up to nine pounds and is one of the newer varieties.

Chinchilla: This is one of the most popular fur breeds. The coat resembles real Chinchilla, the under-colour slate-blue, with a band of pearl with a narrow black line edging. The top coat is grey, brightly ticked with black hairs. This is a smaller rabbit than the Beveren, weighing between five-and-a-half and six-and-a-half pounds. The Chinchilla was one of the earliest of our fur varieties and is still one of the most popular, the pelts being much in demand for coats and glove-making.

Chinchilla Giganta: This is a bigger form of the Chinchilla; it has a similar coat and weighs from seven to eleven pounds.

Silver Fox: Here again there are four colours in the breed: the black fox, blue fox, chocolate fox and lilac fox. These have become very popular in recent years, particularly the black silver fox, which should be jet-black, ticked with longer white hairs. The blue should be a medium blue, the chocolate a dark chocolate-brown, the lilac a pinky dove top coat with dove-coloured undercoat. All should be ticked with white hairs.

These are medium-sized rabbits, weighing from five to seven-and-a-half pounds, and are excellent dual purpose rabbits.

Havana: This is a compact rabbit, weighing from five to seven pounds, with a rich dark chocolate coat with a purplish sheen. This fur is the nearest resemblance to mink found among rabbit pelts, and the Havana has always been a popular pelt rabbit. It has well-developed, meaty joints and a very small percentage of waste in the way of offal and bone. The Havana is one of the older breeds, the first ones being exhibited at Utrecht in 1899. They were introduced into England in 1908.

Lilac: The Lilac is one of our newer varieties and originated as a result of a cross between a Blue Beveren and a Havana about 1922. It is like the Havana, fine-boned and well-fleshed, and its coat should be an even pink shade of dove-colour throughout. It weighs about seven pounds.

The colouring of the Lilac is most attractive, and is especially suitable for making fur garments for younger people.

New Zealand Red: No other variety of rabbit is quite like the

New Zealand Red, either in colour or coat. It is quite a big rabbit, weighing from six to eight pounds, and has a bright reddish buff coat. The coat is very dense and somewhat harsh in texture, and wears extremely well when made up into garments. It has been in this country for about forty years, and is quite popular in some districts. More recently the New Zealand White has made its appearance.

Sable: There are two varieties of Sable, the Marten Sable and the Siamese Sable. The pelts resemble those of the wild sable, and being a good shade of brown, are always popular. There are three shades in each variety—Light, Medium and Dark—and this gives rather a wide range when matching pelts. The colour of the Sable should be a rich sepia on the back, shading off on flanks, chests and sides to a paler colour. The great difference between the Sables is that the Marten Sable has white markings on the legs, belly and feet, and the Siamese Sable has not.

Sable rabbits should weigh from five to seven pounds and make very good table rabbits. Sables, like the Lilacs, are a British production and were introduced about 1919.

Siberian: This is quite a new variety and is found in three colours—black, blue, and brown, the brown-coated ones being the most popular. It has a quite distinctive coat, which is known as a roll back or blanket fur. When brushed in the reverse direction, the fur should give the appearance of having been sheared. This is another medium-sized rabbit, weighing from five to seven pounds.

Smoke Pearl: This is a fascinating variety of a very pretty colour. Like the Sable, it is of two patterns or varieties: the Marten and the Siamese. The saddle should be smoke in colour, shading to pearl, grey, beige on flanks and chest.

The Smoke Pearl should weigh from five to seven pounds. There are a few other normal-coated breeds classed as fur rabbits, including the Beige, the Chifox, Golden Glavcot, and Nubian, but these are not bred in any numbers.

The fur breed which has made tremendous strides during

recent years is the Rex rabbit. These rabbits, which can now be had in a great variety of colours, have soft plush-like coats, lacking the stiff guard hairs which the normal-coated rabbits have. The Rex were first discovered in France, and occurred purely by chance among a litter of normal rabbits. A French priest, M. Gillet, foresaw that rabbits with such a soft plush-like coat would have a great future, and did his best to establish the new variety. The first Rex rabbits imported into this country during the 1920's were unattractive specimens, with thin coats, big ears, and bent legs. These were Castor-Rex—a dark chestnut brown rabbit. Careful and selective breeding has not only given excellent type in Rex, but also many colours to choose from. In fact, most of the normal varieties have been Rexed.

Rex breeds include Ermine (a pure white), Black, Blue, Lilac, Havana (brown), Nutria (a rich golden colour), Smoke Pearl, Orange-buff, Siamese, Sable, Seal, Marten Sable, Orange, Tan, Fawn, Opal (pale blue top with a layer of golden tan between it and the slate under-colour), Lynx (orange shot silver), Chinchilla, Castor-rex, Cinnamin (a bright golden tan).

There are also the marked breeds, including Himalayan-rex, Silver-Seal Rex, English and Dutch.

The Astrex is a curly-coated rabbit.

Rex rabbits weigh from six to eight pounds and make excellent meat rabbits, while their pelts, when in really good condition, fetch higher prices than normal coated varieties. Modern Rex rabbits are quite hardy, and are free from the ailments and disfigurements which marked the first Rex-coated rabbits imported to this country.

Among the fancy breeds we find the *Belgian Hare,* a big racy rabbit, rather more like a hare in appearance. It is one of the oldest varieties and a very popular one. It has a rich chestnut-coloured coat, and weighs eight or nine pounds.

Dutch: This is one of the most popular fancy breeds, and is well known with its white saddle, face markings, and feet. Dutch can be had in black, blue, tortoiseshell, grey, chocolate and yellow. They are very hardy and the does are renowned as good mothers. They are compact little rabbits, weighing about five and a half pounds and make excellent meat rabbits for the small family.

English: The English, with its distinctive spotted coat, is another old variety which has a very wide following. It also can be found in several colours: Black and White, Tortoise and White, Blue and White, Grey and White, and Chocolate and White. It is a rather bigger rabbit than the Dutch, weighing up to eight pounds, but it shares the virtues of the Dutch in that it is hardy; the does make excellent mothers and the youngsters are quick-growing. Although it is classed as a fancy rabbit, the prettily marked pelts make up into attractive pram covers, and evening capes and stoles.

Flemish Giants: These rabbits, as their name implies, are the giants of the rabbit family. They should not weigh less than eleven pounds, but can weigh as much over this as their breeders can achieve. This is the rabbit for those with plenty of room and plenty of food, for such a big rabbit needs space and plenty of material for growth. It should be a dark steel-grey in colour, with even or wavy ticking all over the body. Although classed as a fancy rabbit, Flemish have at times been quite popular as pelt rabbits, for their pelts are very dense and hard-wearing.

Himalayans: This is an old but very attractive variety, being white with black nose and ears, and black 'stockinged' feet. Its original home is said to be China, where it is still to be found in great numbers and is held in high esteem. It is rather small, weighing only about five pounds, but its white pelt is useful for a number of purposes, and it provides a very good carcase.

L ps: Lop, with its long ears, is one of our oldest varieties of domesticated rabbit, and has been known in this country for almost a century. It is known as the King of the Fancy, and is notable for its very long ears, which sweep down to the ground. The following colours are found in Lops: Sooty fawn, fawn, fawn and white, black and white, tortoise and white.

Polish: This dapper little white rabbit is the bantam of the rabbit fancy and weighs only two and a half to three pounds. If the Flemish is the rabbit for the man with plenty of room and food, the Polish suits the man with little of either, for it takes up very little room and is economical to feed. It is very easy to rear and quick-growing, and its lovely and smart appearance have gained it many admirers.

Silvers: This is another of the older breeds and has been popular in this country for a century. It is a well-proportioned, medium-sized rabbit weighing from five to six pounds, and is one of the best meat producers. It can be had in three colours: silver-grey, fawn and brown. The silver-grey is black with a silver effect of white ticking, the fawn is orange with white ticking and the brown a rich deep chestnut with an even mixture of black and silver hairs. The silver-grey is the most popular.

Tans: This is another well-established variety, small and compact, weighing about four and a half pounds. The varieties are black and tan, blue and tan, chocolate and tan, and lilac and tan. Each colour has rich golden tan-coloured markings on the head and chest, and bright tickings on the body.

There are one or two other comparatively rare breeds, but the foregoing list covers the main breeds of both fur and fancy rabbits.

The Angora: The Angora is in a class by itself, as it is the only rabbit bred for wool. There are white and coloured Angoras, but the white is the variety most commonly met with. The rabbit should have a snowball-like appearance with tufts of wool on the ears and feet. These tufts are called 'furnishings' and indicate that the rabbits are good wool producers. The wool should be from two and a half to three inches long to command the best prices, and should be clean and free from mats.

Some breeders may prefer to have cross-bred rabbits for meat production, as these are hardy and grow quickly. The pelts are of little commercial value, because they are usually of various colours and difficult to match. Cross-breds are not such a good proposition as pure-breds, which give an equally good carcase, and also a worth-while pelt, or the pleasure of exhibiting.

For those who want to try cross-breds it is best to have a small buck mated with a larger doe. If the small doe is mated to a large buck, she may have difficulty at kindling time. It is best to make the cross from the pure-bred stock each time. If cross-breds are mated together, faults soon begin to appear and the carcases have an undue proportion of bone and offal.

A Dutch, English, or Silver buck crossed with a Flemish, Beveren or Argenté doe will give a good meaty type of rabbit.

If rabbits of wild grey colouring are desired, Belgian Hares or Silvers, crossed with any other variety, will usually give the desired result.

The Chinchilla Rabbit

The Angora Rabbit

The Dutch Rabbit

Morant Hutches

CHAPTER 2

HOUSING

THE first question which arises when the housing of rabbits is considered is, 'Shall I house my rabbits inside or outside?'

If a building such as a garage, poultry house, garden hut or barn is available, it is a good idea to use it. Hutches which are to be used inside a shelter need not be quite so strong and well made as those which are to be used outside, because they will not have to stand up to such severe weather. If does are to kindle in the early part of the year, when severe frosts may be expected, it is less risky if they kindle in a hutch which is inside a shed. Kindling often takes quite a time and in severe weather some of the litter may be chilled to death before the doe puts them into the nest. If outside hutches are used for winter breeding purposes, the hutch fronts should be protected with sacking to guard against the cold.

Another point in favour of indoor hutches is that it is easier for the owner to attend to the rabbits in bad weather if he is under cover. If no shed is available a lean-to shed made with a galvanised roof will do quite well, especially if it faces South, and is well sheltered from cold winds.

If no shed of any kind can be constructed, there is no need to fear that the rabbits will do badly. Rabbits thrive well in outside hutches provided that the hutches are warm and weather proof. In fact, they are better outside than in a stuffy, badly aired shed. Sheds which house rabbits must always be well ventilated otherwise the rabbits will have perpetual colds.

In outside hutches there is not much risk of colds, or of the spread of infection.

Both inside and outside housing have their advantages and disadvantages, and it is up to each individual rabbit keeper to house his rabbits in the way that suits him best. One thing he must ensure, and that is that the rabbits have ample room, and that their hutches are dry and free from draughts. The tame rabbit is a hardy animal and can stand a great deal of cold, but damp and draughts will prove fatal to it.

People tend to make breeding hutches too small. Rabbits need room to move about, and a doe should be able to get away from her litter if she wants to, and the litter should have room to get the exercise they need for growth. The minimum size for a breeding hutch should be 3 ft. 6 ins. long, 2 ft. 3 ins. wide and from 1 ft. 10 ins. to 2 ft. high. It is most economical of space and building material to make the hutches in stacks of three tiers. It is sometimes possible to get bacon boxes, or sugar boxes in the correct size, and this means that the hutch is half made. If wood has to be bought, $\frac{3}{4}$ inch tongued and grooved boards for back, sides, floor, roof and front is best, and 2 in. × 1 in. quartering for the framework. Some $\frac{3}{4}$ inch mesh wire netting will be needed for the doors, and roofing felt for the roofs if the hutches are to be used out of doors. All hutches should be raised well off the ground, so that a free passage of air round them is assured and the hutches cannot become damp underneath. It also prevents mice and other vermin from making their nests under the hutches.

The framework of a stack of hutches should be made in four sections: back, front and two sides. A stack of three tiers can be made up of any number of separate hutches in units of threes. It can be three, six, nine, twelve and so on, and it is easy to add an additional three hutches when there is an increase of stock. When the framework has been made, make frames for the doors. It is quite a good plan to have a door which opens along the whole length of the hutch with a small wire netting door hinged on it. The netting door should take up about half the length of the hutch if the hutches are for outside use. For inside use the netting door can be made larger as this permits more ventilation.

It is a common fault in home-built hutches to make the door so that it fits badly, and is either too big or too small for the space it is to occupy. If it is too big there is continual trouble in shutting it, and if it is too small it not only admits wind and rain into an outdoor hutch, but also gives the rabbit added opportunity for hutch gnawing.

When making doors, measure carefully to see that they are an exact fit. This will save a great deal of time and trouble later on, and will mean that the rabbits are more securely housed.

When making breeding hutches, fix a shelf almost six inches wide, and about nine inches above the floor of the hutch, running from front to back of the hutch behind the wooden door. This will enable the doe to get away from her hungry litter if she wants to. Just before weaning time young rabbits often worry the doe unnecessarily for milk, and if she cannot get away from them for a time, she may turn savage. Such a shelf also gives the youngsters more room in the hutch when the doe is not occupying the floor space.

Another thing which is most useful in a breeding hutch is a hutch board. This is a board about three inches high, which fits just behind the door and remains in position when the door is opened. The board forms a barrier which prevents litter and bedding from falling on to the floor when the door is opened, and it also prevents the young rabbits from falling out. Young rabbits have a habit of crowding to the door when it is opened, particularly at feeding time, and if they are in the top hutch, a fall to the ground can be fatal.

The hutch board should not be a fixture, otherwise it will make cleaning out difficult. A slot to take the board can be made quite easily by nailing narrow battens on either side of the hutch, so that the board can be lifted out when the hutch needs cleaning.

Some breeders build their hutches with a floor which slopes slightly towards the back, and projects a little beyond the back of the hutch. This is to allow the moisture to drain out, and fall to the ground away from the back of the hutch. If the floors are solid and well built, there is no need to use a sloping floor.

If the hutch floors are well creosoted, and sanded while the creosote is still wet, this will help to keep them waterproof. The entire stack of hutches should be given one or two coats of creosote both inside and out. This helps to preserve the wood, and is a precaution against infection if old wood has been used for hutch building. The creosote must be given plenty of time to dry before the hutches are used.

If the hutches are for inside use, they need no extra roofing, but if they are to be used outside, the roof must be covered with roofing felt and made with a backward slope. To obtain this backward slope, reduce the length of the back uprights by about 3 inches. It is a good plan to make the roofs of outdoor hutches project about a yard beyond the front of the hutches. This serves the double purpose of sheltering the hutch from rain, and it also protects the rabbits' owner when feeding or attending to the animals in wet weather. A hay rack should be made at the side of the hutch about six inches from the floor. This is usually more satisfactory than a wire netting rack to hang on the door.

When finishing off the hutch make sure that there are no rough edges of wire netting anywhere on which the rabbits may damage themselves.

Smaller hutches for single rabbits can be made on the stack or battery system in the same way. A good sized hutch for a single rabbit is 2 ft. 6 ins. long by 2 ft. wide by 1 ft. 10 ins. high. This gives room for the rabbit to move about freely, and is a very suitable hutch for pelt rabbits which have to be housed separately.

Where rabbits are not intended for the production of prime pelts, they can be housed together in indoor colonies or runs. Rabbits do well on this system, because it gives them ample room and opportunity for exercise. Colonies of this type can be made in an outhouse or garage, or in a lean-to shed. The pens can be made with wire netting of 1 inch mesh, mounted on wood framing of 2 x 1 inch. The usual floor space allowed in a colony pen is 2 square feet for each rabbit, and it is not advisable to run more than 25 rabbits in one colony. This is because rabbits in colonies are rather easily frightened, and will stampede in a mad rush if a stranger is seen, or they are startled by an unusual noise. If there are too many rabbits together, these stampedes may cause one or two of them to be injured.

When making colonies in a shed or out-building it is necessary to see that the shed is vermin proof, and that there are no floor draughts. If the floor is made of concrete, plenty of straw should be used as litter, and it is an advantage to put a raised sleeping board at one end. Some breeders give the rabbits a large box to sleep in, particularly if the colony is in a lean-to shed, as this gives them warmer sleeping quarters. Hayracks can be made on each wire netting partition, and if there are several separate pens, one hay rack can be built to serve two pens.

Colonies of young rabbits may be made up of one litter, or of several litters of the same age. They will live together quite peacefully up to about four months old, but must then be separated into sexes. The does will run together until needed for breeding or for table purposes, but bucks must be housed separately after this age or they will fight.

Morant Hutches.—During late spring and summer and for a part of the autumn, rabbits can be housed out of doors in Morant Hutches. The Morant system is a method of raising rabbits in batches of six or eight in movable hutches which have wire netting floors. The hutches are placed on grass, and are moved daily. This does away with cleaning out, except for the small covered sleeping compartment which is quickly and easily dealt with, and to some extent with the labour of feeding. Rabbits cannot be expected to get all the food they require from grazing the grass available when the Morant hutch is moved, but they will get quite a big proportion of it. When rabbits are housed in Morant hutches feeding costs are very small, but it is essential that the grass the rabbits are getting is good grass containing a variety of herbage. In addition to what they can pick for themselves, rabbits need some hay daily, and a little mash two or three times a week. If the green food is sparse or of poor quality, they will need some wild green food, or garden greens in addition.

There are several possible designs for Morant hutches, but each has the same essentials. The hutch must be reasonably light so that it can be moved easily, and must be fitted with handles for ease in lifting. One part of the hutch must be covered in as a protection against the weather, and the covered in part can have a board floor raised slightly from the ground. This serves as sleeping quarters for the rabbits, as it is not advisable for them to sleep on the ground. Some breeders prefer to make the floor or the covered part of the hutch of netting and to put raised sleeping shelves round the side. Either way is satisfactory.

The Morant hutch itself should be about 7 ft. long, 3 ft. wide, and rise to an apex 2 ft. 9 ins. high. The covered part of the hutch should be about 3 ft. long. Four triangles should be constructed of 2 in. × 1 in. battens each 3 ft. long. A fifth triangle should be made and boarded in, with a hole cut for the rabbits to go in and out. The hutch should open completely at either end. The netting used should be 2 inch mesh at the bottom of the run, and 1 inch mesh for the sides. If roofing felt is used for the covered part of the hutch, the whole of the sides should be covered with netting.

Young rabbits can be put into a Morant hutch at eight weeks old. It is best to put them into the hutch for the first time on a mild sunny day, and as with indoor colonies it is best to sex them before they are put into the hutches.

If young pelt rabbits are put into Morant hutches it is best to provide the hutch with some sort of shade, for although sunshine and fresh air are good for the rabbits, too much sun will fade their coats. Pelt rabbits really need separate hutches at from four to five months.

The full use of Morant hutches means that there must be ample ground to work on, because it is not advisable to graze the same piece of ground too frequently. If it is used too often the ground will become sour, and will cause stomach upsets to the rabbits which feed upon it. Each plot of grass should be lightly dusted with lime when it is vacated, and a really good crop of grass should be allowed to grow on it before it is used again. The same patch of ground can be used two or three times in a season, according to how rapidly the grass grows again. Care should be taken to see that the ground used for Morant hutches has not been fouled by dogs, otherwise tape-worm infection may cause trouble.

Morants can be used with success for about six months of the year, and often when the weather is too bad to have them outside they can be used to house rabbits inside a shed; Morant raised rabbits are usually hardy and suffer from few ailments: They do not mind dry cold, but excessive wet and fog are the things to guard against. Such outside hutches must also be well protected against the rabbits' natural enemies, such as dogs, cats, weasels, stoats and rats.

Free Range.—Rabbits can be bred and reared successfully on a free range. Poultry pens can be converted for this purpose, but to prevent the rabbits from burrowing out of such a pen, a wire mat, at least 2 ft. wide, should be laid on the ground inside the fence. This will prevent any risk of escape, as rabbits nearly always begin to burrow as near the edge of their enclosure as they can get. The guard fence round a free range of this sort should be about 6 ft. high, to prevent other animals from getting in. Wire netting of 2 inch mesh will do for the main part of the fence, but this is not proof against stoats and weasels, so netting of a small mesh should be used at the bottom of the fence. Cats will not usually attempt to climb a fence of this height, but should any do so, a 12 inch strand of wire netting at right angles on the top of the fence will prevent them from getting to the rabbits. About 7 sq. ft. of space per rabbit is a liberal amount of room in free range colonies.

When making up a pen of this sort, it is usual to use one buck with about a dozen does. The adult does will live together quite peacefully once they become used to each other, but bucks can never be relied on not to fight. Some breeders supply the does with boxes, or underground shelters, in which to produce their litters. Most breeders, however, prefer to take the does out of the colony and allow them to kindle in hutches. The difficulty with this system is that it is impossible to be sure when the doe is due to kindle, so it is necessary to remove all the does to hutches from about the twenty-fifth day after the buck was put in. The does will need to be kept in the hutches for thirty-one days after being removed from the colony, if they have not kindled before, because it is always possible that mating took place on the last day before the doe was removed.

The young rabbits, with their mothers, should be allowed to remain in the breeding hutches until they are five or six weeks old, then they can go back to the free range colony if the weather is good.

This system makes it very difficult to keep a rabbit's pedigree, because the youngsters get very mixed up, and a doe will often suckle youngsters which do not belong to her. The only accurate way of marking the youngsters is by ringing or tattooing. If young rabbits are being bred for meat purposes this system is quite a good one, and saves labour, but it is not a good system for fur production, or for the production of pedigree breeding stock. Stock run in free range of this type do very well if they are well fed, but they do need additional food to what they can gather for themselves. Plenty of greens should be given, and also some mash and hay. The green food can be tipped out on the ground, but it is a good idea to have some sort of container for the hay, and certainly the mash must be fed from small troughs, otherwise it will be wasted.

Colony rabbits must be securely shut up at night in some type of shelter. This not only means that they will be safe during the night, but allows the breeder to keep his stock under regular observation. If the stock are checked when shut up at night, and also when let out in the morning, any ailing rabbit can be spotted and, if necessary, removed from the colony.

If any difficulty is experienced in 'rounding up' the stock at night, this can be overcome quite easily by giving the rabbits their last feed just before it is time to shut them up. They soon get to know when it is feeding time and will go into the shelter quite readily in search of food.

CHAPTER 3

FEEDING

THE first principle in feeding rabbits is to provide them with a varied and well-balanced diet; the second, to see that their meal times are regular. They can be fed twice or three times a day, according to the owner's convenience, but they should always be fed as nearly as possible at the same time each day. Irregular feeding leads to stomach upsets and is a frequent cause of death among young rabbits.

Rabbits need some proteins, because these are flesh- and muscle-forming. Protein is particularly necessary for young rabbits when they are growing, and a certain amount is necessary for adult stock to replace worn out tissues. Protein is found in hay and straw, and in some degree in roots and greenstuff, but the biggest proportion of protein is found in oats, maize, and meals, such as barley meal, maize meal, soya bean meal, etc.

Rabbits also need some carbohydrates to provide energy and warmth. These too are found in oats, wheat, maize, and the various meals, and in potato and scrap mash. Mineral salts and vitamins are essential for the maintenance of health, particularly among young stock. Fortunately these necessary vitamins are found in clover, hay, green plants, and roots, so there is little danger of rabbits suffering from a deficiency of vitamins, since one or more of the vitamins are present in all the natural food used for them.

Rabbits need a concentrated meal of mash or oats, some hay and greenfood or roots daily. Individual rabbits vary considerably in the amount they will eat, and each one should be studied so that it gets enough food but that none is wasted. A rough guide to the amount of food an average-sized adult rabbit needs is half a pound of mash or one to two ounces of oats, about one pound of greens or half a pound of roots, and two or three ounces of hay daily. Bigger breeds will need more than this, smaller breeds rather less. A doe suckling youngsters will need considerably more, and should be given up to one pound of mash, or four ounces of oats, and as much hay and greenstuff as she will eat. Unless she has plenty of food, the young rabbits will lack stamina, and fall easy victims to any disease that may be prevalent.

It is a good plan to give the feed of mash or oats in the morning, when the rabbits are really hungry and clear it up readily. A good mash can be made with potato peelings, or small potatoes boiled in their skins. The potatoes or peelings must be cleaned before being boiled with a pinch of salt. They should be mashed while they are warm, and any household scraps, such as crumbs, chopped bacon rind, cheese, plate scrapings or fish waste can be added. The mash should be dried off until it is crumbly with a good broad bran or oatmeal. Mash should be fed soon after mixing as it soon becomes sour if it is left standing about. It should always be fed from bowls, never put on the floor of the hutch, and food bowls must always be kept clean.

Instead of a potato mash, various meal mixtures may be used for rabbit feeding, or they can be given oats. Oats, whole or crushed, are a very well-balanced food and are more widely used for rabbit feeding than any other grain. Wheat can be used, but when it is used, it is usually mixed with oats. About the same amount of mixed oats and wheat, that is, about two ounces should be used.

Useful meal mixtures for rabbits include:—

(1) Three parts bran to one part of middlings and a quarter part best white fish meal.
(2) Four parts maize meal, four parts Sussex ground oats, one part broad bran, and one part white fish meal.
(3) Equal proportions of pea or bean meal, bran, crushed oats, and barley meal or sharps.
(4) Two parts dried brewers' grains, two parts barley or maize meal, one part white fish meal.

These meal mixtures may be fed dry, or the bran or brewers'

grains used may be soaked with an equal weight of water for several hours, then dried off by adding the allowance of meal mixture. Only enough for one mash should be made up at a time, as the mash soon sours, particularly in hot weather. A useful addition to the mash is sugar-beet pulp, which has a high food value. This should always be soaked over-night before being used.

Pellet feeding has now been introduced for rabbits. The pellets are a perfectly-balanced diet, and only hay and drinking water need be given in addition. A rabbit should have approximately five or six ounces a day of the pellets, but again individual appetites must be studied.

If the rabbits are given a concentrated meal of mash or oats in the morning, give greens or roots at midday and hay at night. If no midday feed can be given, put some hay or greenfood in the racks after the mash has been given, so that the rabbits can eat when they feel hungry, and give more greens or roots and some hay at night.

Wild greenfoods suitable for rabbits will be dealt with in a subsequent chapter. Always feed as big a variety of these as possible, for to a rabbit, variety in greenfood is literally the 'spice of life'. Greenfoods contain vitamins and minerals vital to the rabbit's well-being, and it needs a certain amount of each. Too much of one particular kind is often as bad as too little, and a variety of greens ensures that the animal gets all it needs in the way of minerals and vitamins. Almost all the greens grown in the garden for human consumption are suitable for rabbits, and here again a mixture of several kinds is better than a lot of one kind.

Roots suitable for rabbits include beet, sugar beet, artichokes, swedes, carrots, kohl-rabi and mangolds. A comparatively new root crop for rabbit feeding is Fodder Beet. This has twice the feeding value of mangolds, is not likely to cause stomach upsets, and is a fine conditioner. The tops are good food, too, but they should be well wilted before being fed to stock. A constant supply of greenfood can be obtained by stripping a few leaves at a time from each plant. White or Red Otofte are suitable varieties to grow.

If mangolds are used for rabbit feeding, they should be kept until January, when they become ripe and mellow. They will keep in good condition longer than any other root crop, which is another reason for keeping them until other roots have been used up. As with potatoes for the mash, roots *must* be cleaned before being fed. Dirt accumulates in a rabbit's stomach and causes digestive troubles. Roots can be fed in pieces the size of a cricket ball or can be cut into fingers. Hay should be fed at night-time and some should be available in the racks during the day-time. The best hay for rabbits is clover hay or good meadow hay. Hay is expensive, and many rabbit keepers make their own, and so save expense. Grass from waste land and road verges, if cut while it is young and tender and then well dried, makes excellent hay for rabbits, and so do young stinging nettles. Nettle hay has been proved to be almost as nutritious as clover hay, and better than poor quality meadow hay. Nettles lose their sting when dried and rabbits are very fond of dried nettle hay.

Good leafy samples of straw, such as oat straw, are also very useful for rabbit feeding. Never use damp or mouldy hay, or straw, or samples which are very dusty. Good hay should look bright and clean and have a pleasant smell not unlike tobacco.

Acorns make excellent food for rabbits, and some should be dried during autumn for winter feeding purposes. If possible gather the acorns on a dry day, but if they are wet when gathered, they will dry well if spread out thinly on a wooden floor and turned several times a week until dry. If the acorns are heaped before they are completely dry, they will begin to germinate and will be useless for feeding purposes.

Acorns can either be fed whole or can be crushed, or ground into meal for drying off the mash. Up to ten per cent of the mash can be made of ground acorn meal, or a small handful of acorns can be given to each rabbit. When dry, the shells of acorns are very hard, and it is necessary to crack them before giving them to rabbits. Acorns are an acquired taste and some rabbits do not take to them on first acquaintance, but they soon acquire a liking for them and eat them readily.

Another useful addition to the diet is clean potato peelings crisped in the oven until they are somewhat like flaked maize. These can be used occasionally instead of the mash or oat feed.

Here are some 'Don'ts' to remember in connection with feeding:—

Don't make sudden changes in diet. Any new kind of green-food or roots must be introduced gradually. Rabbits, like human beings, produce certain enzymes for dealing with certain types of food. A sudden change of diet means that the juices to deal with it are not present in the rabbit's stomach, and so it ferments, causing indigestion or scours.

Don't feed frosted greenfood or roots. These do not always have a bad effect, but sometimes they do, particularly where young rabbits are concerned, and it is not worth taking the risk. Thaw frozen roots out in a bucket of cold water—warm water will make them flabby and unappetising.

Don't gather greenfood from places where it is likely to have been soiled by dogs. Many dogs suffer from tape-worm, and soiled greenfood will set up tape-worm cysts in the rabbit. If you are doubtful about any greens you gather, immerse them in salt water and leave to dry for twelve hours before feeding. This will destroy the germs.

Don't leave grass or other greens in a heap to become heated and discoloured. If you are not going to use them at once, spread them out thinly.

The tame rabbit is most accommodating in its diet. It will live and thrive very largely on the waste greenfood and scraps from the house, in addition to wild greens which are free for the gathering. All it needs is regular meal times, a varied and plentiful diet, and clean food from clean feeding vessels.

CHAPTER 4

WILD GREENFOOD, CULTIVATED CROPS FOR RABBITS

INTRODUCTION

To keep rabbits in good health, a large part of their diet should be a natural one, and the natural diet of a wild rabbit is greenfood. Not only are wild greens good for rabbits, but they cost nothing and so cut down the cost of rabbit-feeding considerably.

Very few greenfoods will cause harm to the rabbits, unless they are given in large quantities, but it is a mistake to give whole feeds of one particular greenfood. It is far safer, and better for the rabbits, if a variety of greenfood is used. Greenfood for rabbits should always be gathered from open spaces which get plenty of sunshine. Coarse, lush greenfood that grows in the shade may cause outbreaks of disease. Mildewed plants should never be used, nor those attacked by blight or fungus.

Wild greenfoods suitable for rabbits include:

Avens.—Somewhat resembles the garden geum, with a small yellow flower. Can be found early in spring and summer. Is astringent and useful for counteracting scours.

Agrimony.—Long, tapering spikes of yellow flowers. Blooms in July and August. Has tonic properties and is also useful to prevent scours.

Bramble.—The tender tips and leaves of the common bramble or blackberry make useful rabbit food in the spring.

Burnet.—This is a useful and well-known plant, sometimes grown as fodder.

Broom.—The common yellow broom can be used for feeding,

but it is very laxative and should be used in small quantities only.

Cow Parsnip (or Hogweed).—This is one of the most useful weeds for rabbits with its big, dark green leaves. It bears flat heads of white flowers in July and August.

Cleavers or Goosegrass.—This well-known climbing plant, with its round clinging seed vessels, is very abundant in the spring, and has quite a good feeding value. It is laxative, so should be introduced gradually.

Clovers.—Clovers are too well-known to need description. Both the red and the white varieties make excellent rabbit food.

Comfrey.—Large, coarse-leaved plant found in ditches or other moist places. Has white, pink or purple flowers.

Coltsfoot.—The leaves are heart-shaped, and are downy on the underside. They appear after the flowers, which look like small dandelions and bloom in March. They are good, safe food for rabbits.

Chickweed.—A very common weed in most gardens. It is not of great feeding value, but can be found almost all the year round, and the rabbits enjoy it when other greenfood is scarce.

Dandelion.—This well-known plant is one of the best green-foods for rabbits. It has a valuable tonic effect, but also has a very strong effect on the kidneys, and should not be used in large quantities. A little mixed with other greens will get the best results, and prove beneficial to stock of all ages.

Dock.—There are three varieties of dock, Broad-leaved, Curled, and Sorrel dock. All can be used in moderation before they have seeded, but should never be used after. The young tender leaves can safely be used in the spring. Sorrel dock or Sour dock is the one most enjoyed by rabbits.

Gout Weed.—Gout weed or ground elder is another common weed, which is often a nuisance in gardens. This can be used for feeding before the flowers appear, but should be discontinued in the flowering and seeding stage.

Groundsel.—This is another common weed which proves a nuisance to gardeners. It can usually be found almost all the year round. It is rather laxative, so should be given in small quantities, when it has a stimulating effect. Does which are reluctant to mate, and rabbits which 'stick in the moult' will benefit by having a few sprays of groundsel daily. Plants which show signs of an orange-coloured fungus should be avoided.

Heather.—The young tender shoots of heather make quite a useful rabbit food for those who live in districts where heather is abundant. It should not be used when it gets old and tough.

Hawk Bit and Hawk Weed.—These are commonly found on road verges and in lanes. There are a number of varieties, but they all have flowers very similar to small dandelions on slender stems. Can be used in a mixture with other greens.

Hedge Parsley.—One of the most useful wild plants for rabbit-feeding. Appears early in the spring, and can be fed safely until the plant flowers. The leaves are very much cut and the flowers grow in flat heads, while the stem is grooved. Can be found in sheltered places as early as February.

Knapweed.—This pinkish-purple flower, growing from a hard black calyx, is found in meadows. It will not provide much in the way of greenfood, but is useful in increasing the variety of plant food.

Knotgrass.—Found in large quantities on waste ground or by the roadsides. They have greenish-white flowers. Quite a valuable green food which rabbits eat with relish.

Mallow.—The flowers are pink or mauve, and can be found on waste ground and roadsides. This plant has a high nutritive value, and no ill effects will ever occur as a result of using mallow as a greenfood.

Nipplewort.—A leafy plant with sprays of small pale yellow flowers. Should be used whenever it can be found, as it is always much enjoyed by rabbits.

Nettle.—Dead nettles may be used in the fresh green state. They have quite a high feeding value, and rabbits enjoy them in spite of their rather pungent smell.

Stinging nettles should never be used when fresh, but when

dried they lose their sting and make most excellent hay for winter use. Nettles, if cut early in the year, will grow again and give a good second crop.

Plantain.—There are two types of plantain—broad-leaved plantain and long-leaved plantain. Both these make good rabbit food, and as they are both slightly astringent, it is a good plan to include some of these greens in the greenfood mixture in early spring, when most plants tend to be rather laxative.

Shepherd's Purse.—A common weed, with small white flowers, and a seed-pod like an old-fashioned purse. This is an astringent plant also, and is most useful in checking cases of scours among young rabbits. It has a tonic effect, and many rabbit-breeders like to dry a quantity of the weeds for use during the winter.

Sow Thistle (or Milk Thistle).—This resembles the common thistle, but does not prick and has yellow flowers instead of purple ones. When the stem is broken a milky substance exudes. Most useful for pregnant and nursing does, and quite safe to give to stock of all ages.

Trefoil.—There are a number of trefoils, most of them of creeping habit, and resembling small clover plants. It is a valuable food in the green state and dries well for winter use.

Vetch (or Tares).—Climbing plants with pea-like leaves and pods, and red-yellow or purple flowers. All varieties are useful as rabbit food.

Water-cress.—Can sometimes be found growing wild in ditches and streams. Rabbits off their food can often be tempted to begin eating if given a small amount of watercress. Should not be fed after the plants have flowered, when it becomes very strong-flavoured.

Yarrow.—This has dark green leaves which are found close to the ground. The leaves are cut into many thin segments. The flowers grow in a flat head and are white or pinkish. Will not provide a lot of greenfood, but is useful because of its tonic properties.

There are a number of wild plants which should not be fed to rabbits. These include, Anemone, Wild Arum, Autumn Crocus, Buttercup (this is harmless when dried), Bluebells, Belladonna or Deadly Nightshade, Black Nightshade, Bryony, Bindweed, Celandine, Dog Mercury, Elder, Figwort, Foxglove, Fool's Parsley, Hemlock, Henbane, Poppies, Toad Flax and Travellers' Joy.

Probably the most dangerous wild plant for rabbits is Hemlock. It is rather similar in appearance to Hedge Parsley, and is sometimes gathered in mistake for it. Hemlock is a tall plant, growing from three to six feet high. It has a smooth stem, while Hedge Parsley has a grooved one. The stem is hollow, bright green in colour and marked with reddish-purple spots. If the stems are crushed, they have a disagreeable strong smell, and this is perhaps the easiest way to distinguish between Hemlock and Hedge Parsley.

Wild greens will provide the rabbit with all the succulent food it needs during spring and summer, and for some time during the autumn, but the rabbit-breeder should grow some crops in his garden to feed his stock during the winter months, and to provide for periods of drought in summertime, when wild greens are poor in quality.

Crops which can be grown in quite a small garden and which will produce plenty of good food for rabbits include:

Artichokes.—Jerusalem variety. These grow well on poor ground, need little attention, and can be left on the same piece of ground for several years. They have good feeding value and rabbits like them. They can be left in the ground until they are needed without being harmed by frost. The roots can be used raw as a root feed, or cooked as part of the mash. The tops and stems can also be used as greenfood.

Beetroot.—Beet is an excellent food for rabbits, and both the garden beet and sugar beet should be grown for them. Rabbits never seem to tire of beetroot and will often eat it eagerly when they have been 'off their feed' as regards other foods.

Sugar beet is an admirable food for does and litters, its high sugar content making it very nourishing. It is particularly useful when changing the root diet, as it never causes scouring as some roots do if fed in large quantities at first.

Chicory.—This is the rabbit fancier's favourite crop. It is a most valuable greenfood, will thrive practically anywhere, and multiplies rapidly. Giant Witloof is the best variety to grow for use as greenfood. The outside leaves can be picked every ten days or so, and the plant keeps growing through summer and autumn, in fact, until the sharp frosts begin. Chicory is an excellent conditioner, and those who show rabbits will find that it helps to impart that extra 'bloom' to the fur which is so important.

Carrots.—Carrots are rich in sugar, easily digested, and very much enjoyed by rabbits of all ages. They are particularly useful for does and young litters. The thinnings of the crop can be used as greenfood and can be fed in generous quantities. The tops of the mature roots also make a useful contribution to the greenfood mixture, but should not be fed in such quantities as the earlier thinnings.

Cabbage.—As a general rule, the waste from cabbages used in the kitchen supplies sufficient greens for a few rabbits. If a few spring cabbages are grown for rabbit-feeding, they should not be allowed to heart up. The green leaves are best for rabbits. If the stumps are left, they will sprout again and give a useful second crop.

Kohl Rabi.—This root is not as well-known as the more usual ones grown for rabbits, but it deserves to be more popular. It can be fed with safety from October onwards, and can be left in the ground until needed, as it will resist frosts. It also has a good resistance to drought and grows well when other roots fail. The tops make good greenfood and should be pulled off and fed fresh.

Kales.—These are the main-stay of rabbits during the winter months. Marrowstem, Thousand Head, and Hungry-gap are the most useful kinds. The bottom leaves can be picked for feeding purposes and the top of the plant will continue to grow and put out more leaves, or small branching 'heads', in the case of

Thousand Head. When the plants are pulled up the stems can be split into quarters so that the rabbits can get at the juicy insides. Cabbage stems and brussels sprouts stems can be treated in the same way.

No member of the brassica family should be used when it has begun to flower.

Lucerne.—If you have room to spare, a good bed of lucerne will provide a good supply of greens. It will stand for about seven years, and can be cut four or five times each season. The roots go down a tremendous depth, and the plants withstand severe drought. If the lucerne is not needed as a greenfood during the summer, it makes very good hay for winter use.

Lettuce.—Although many people regard lettuce as a good rabbit food, it should never be given in large quantities. A leaf or two included in the greenfood mixture for adult stock is much enjoyed, but it should not be fed to young stock, and should be used in moderation for older rabbits.

Sunflowers.—These may seem more of a decorative plant than a food crop, but they do supply a variety of food for rabbits. The leaves can be picked off and fed fresh, and the seed heads stored for winter use. A dozen seeds every other day, crushed and added to the mash, make a useful article of diet for adult stock owing to the quantity of oil they contain.

Swedes.—Swedes have a high feeding value and a long period of usefulness, which makes them one of the best root crops for rabbit feeding. Swedes should be pulled up and stored inside a shed, or clamped, as they will not withstand frost. They can be used from October until April.

Root-storing.—If you have no room to store roots in a shed, it will be necessary to clamp them. To do this, lay a covering of dry straw, about four inches thick, on the ground where the roots are to be clamped. Choose as sheltered and dry a spot as possible then build the roots up into an apex, and cover them with another layer of straw about three inches thick. As a further protection, about six inches of soil, taken from the outside edges of the clamp, should be put on evenly. The removal of soil from round the clamp makes a trench which serves as a drain to keep the clamp dry. Straw ventilators should be made about every four feet along the top of the clamp.

Storing Dried Greens, Nettles and Hay.—If these are stored in sacks, the sacks must be raised from the ground, otherwise the contents will become damp and mouldy. The sacks can be raised on pieces of wood, or hung from the roof.

In connection with dried greenfoods, lawn mowings are very valuable, being equal to good quality hay. Short mowings are also useful to dry off the mash when bran is scarce. Mowings can be spread out on roof-tops or concrete paths, and turned occasionally until they are completely dry. A large quantity can be stored in sacks for winter feeding.

When to Use Crops Grown for Winter Feeding.—Marrow-stem kale is at its best in October, and should be used before other kales. To make the best use of this kale, split the large stalks and give these to the rabbits as well as the greens.

Kohl-rabi is best used in November and December, as it does not keep long after Christmas. Vary the feeding of marrow-stem kale and kohl-rabi, so that the rabbits do not get too much of one food at a time.

By December, beet, swedes, and carrots are at their best, but these will all keep on into January and February, so should be used moderately until the kohl-rabi is finished. Swedes do not keep well after February. Sugar beet will keep a little longer, so use the swedes first.

In March the thousand-headed kale is good, and mangolds at their best. Mangolds can be used from January on if necessary, but should always be saved till last as they keep longer than any other root.

In April the thousand-headed or hungry-gap kale will carry on until the wild greens are plentiful.

CHAPTER 5

STOCK-CHOOSING AND GENERAL MANAGEMENT

EVEN the newcomer to rabbit-breeding can make sure that the rabbits he buys are in good health if he knows what signs to look for. If you are buying rabbits of any particular breed, it is a good plan to go to a few rabbit shows, and study the winning exhibits in the breed you fancy. This will help the novice to learn about the breed standard, which he should also obtain and study.

But apart from getting a rabbit which is true to type, and a good specimen of its particular breed, it is essential to buy rabbits which are healthy. One of the first things to notice is the rabbit's nose. It should be clean and free from any sign of discharge. Running noses in rabbits mean either a cold, which is not always easy to cure and may affect other stock, or worse still, snuffles, which is in many cases impossible to cure, and which will also affect other rabbits very quickly. If the front paws of a rabbit appear wet or sticky, this is often because it has been trying to wipe the mucus from its nose with its paws. Rabbits which sneeze should be avoided too. A sneeze may only be caused by dust or by a foreign body in the rabbits' nostrils, but it is also one of the signs of colds and snuffles.

In addition to a clean nose, a rabbit should be bright-eyed. Dull eyes denote either illness of some kind or old age. Rabbits with running eyes should never be purchased for breeding purposes.

Rabbits should be lively in expression and movement. One of the first and most persistent signs of illness is dullness and lethargy. If a rabbit sits moping in its hutch, it is almost always a sign of illness, and means that the animal should be isolated in case it is suffering from something that can be passed on to the remainder of the stock.

Always look at the ears of any rabbit you intend to purchase.

These should be quite clean inside—scabs and waxy deposits indicate the presence of ear canker. This is quite easy to cure, but it is also infectious, and it is not worth the risk of introducing a rabbit with canker into a healthy stud of rabbits.

Unless a rabbit is going through a natural moulting period, its coat should be sleek and glossy. A coat which appears rough and open is generally called a 'staring' coat and is a sure sign of poor condition. When buying Rex rabbits, see that the undersides of the hocks are well covered with fur. A rabbit should be clean at the back, and its droppings should be round and firm.

Scabs round the vent indicate vent disease or rabbit syphilis. This, like ear canker, is not difficult to cure, but rabbits suffering from it should not be used for breeding until they are quite free from infection. It is passed on from one rabbit to another at breeding times.

A healthy rabbit should feel firm to the touch, and should have a nice firm 'roll' of flesh on either side of the backbone, while the rest of the body should be well-covered with flesh.

When buying new stock always buy from a reliable and well-established breeder. It is usually possible to buy stock on the approval system, which means that no money is paid until the buyer has seen and approved of the stock he wishes to buy.

New stock should always be kept isolated from others for a few days after buying. Then if they have any undetected ailment, it will probably show before they are housed with the rest of the stock, and so prevent the infection being spread.

Another precaution which should be taken is to get full details of the rabbit's diet, and feeding times. These may differ substantially from those of its new owner, and while it will do the rabbit no harm to change to different food, and meal-times, if the change is gradual, it may upset it seriously if the change is made suddenly.

Watch newly-bought stock for a few days to see that they are eating well, are lively and that their droppings are firm and round. They can then be added to the stud, and used for breeding purposes.

Hints on Management.—Apart from the feeding, the job which must be done regularly is cleaning out. Rabbits will do far better in clean, sweet-smelling hutches than they will in dirty ones. Cleaning out should be done twice a week as a general rule, and a doe with a young litter will need cleaning out almost every day. A good absorbent, such as sawdust, peat moss, or ashes should be put on the floor of the hutch, particularly in the 'used' corner, and this should be covered with a layer of straw. Wheat, barley or oat straw is best for this, but if straw is difficult to obtain, dried grass, bracken or dried leaves can be used. In summer-time a little mild disinfectant sprinkled on the hutch floor before adding the fresh litter helps to keep away flies.

Hutches should be given a thorough cleaning at regular intervals. A useful hutch scraping tool can be made from an old hoe, fitted to a short handle, or special cleaning tools may be bought. If a hutch is empty for a short period, it should be well scrubbed out with a strong solution of household ammonia. This helps to get rid of any germs that may linger in the cracks of the wood. When the hutch is dry, it can be given a coat of creosote or lime-wash. Limewash is best for all lightcoated rabbits.

If the rabbits are housed in a shed, keep the rabbitry floor free from litter. Litter of any kind encourages pests. For this reason it is a bad plan to store loose hay or straw under the rabbit hutches. Hutches should always stand slightly away from the walls, both to allow a free current of air round them and also to prevent vermin from making a home there.

Every effort should be made to exclude vermin from the rabbitry. Not only do they spoil and destroy food, but they frighten the rabbits and carry dirt and disease wherever they go.

Hutch Gnawing.—Keep a sharp look out for hutch gnawers. Once a rabbit gets this bad habit, it is difficult to check it. If a rabbit shows signs of gnawing at its hutch, provide it with something else to gnaw. A small log of wood with the bark on, a big bone, or even a handful of twigs will often keep a rabbit happily occupied, so that it forgets about gnawing the hutch. If it continues to do this in spite of attempts to divert it, cut some strips of tin from an ordinary household tin, and tack them firmly over the exposed edges of the hutch that the rabbit can gnaw.

Examine your hutches regularly to see that they are free from leaks or cracks which will cause draughts. Damp and draughts are both a menace to the well-being of tame rabbits.

All rabbits should be examined regularly to see that they are in good condition. This enables the rabbit-breeder to detect any disease in its very early stages, when a complete cure can often be brought about with very little trouble. Ears and vents should be given particular attention.

Rabbits' nails grow longer as they grow older, and need clipping if they get over-long. Long, twisted nails are not only uncomfortable for the rabbit, but if a doe with youngsters has over-long nails, she may easily injure the young rabbits when she goes in and out of the nest at feeding time. Rabbits' nails can be clipped with a pair of sharp wire cutters or pliers. Snip off a little at a time, cutting only the whitish dried-up portion of the nail.

When lifting a rabbit never lift it by the ears alone. A rabbit's ears may be long, but they were never intended by nature to be used as handles to support the weight of the whole body. The weight of the rabbit should be supported by one hand under the hind legs or rump, and the other hand should steady the animal by a gentle grip at the back of the neck. Rabbits which are to be exhibited should be handled frequently, and always spoken to gently, so that they become used to handling and are not nervous when shown. Does in kindle should be handled as little as possible.

Records.—It is a good plan to keep records of all stock to be used for breeding purposes. A record book of this kind will prove most helpful when selecting youngsters for breeding. Under the number, or name of each doe should be put the number of young in a litter, the number successfully weaned, and points as to the doe's qualities as a mother, quantity of milk, etc. It is then simple to select breeding stock from the litters of those does which reared their families successfully without loss, or check in growth. A doe's good qualities in this respect are nearly always passed on to her progeny. Bad qualities are passed on too, and that is why it is not advisable to breed from spiteful does, which are difficult to handle and feed.

Bucks should be chosen from average-sized litters of well-developed youngsters. Bucks taken from small litters may be bigger, but by constantly using bucks from small litters, the average size of the litters would tend to become smaller.

Rabbits which take a long time to moult should also be noted in the book of records. Slow moulters are a nuisance in any rabbitry. They hold up breeding and pelting operations and sometimes begin a fresh moult almost before they have finished the previous one. These loose-coated rabbits are sometimes the result of breeding from moulting breeding stock, but slowness in the moult is an inherited defect, so slow moulters should not be chosen as breeding stock.

Moulting is a natural process, but the rabbit is more liable to become chilled when it is losing its coat, and a rabbit in heavy moult should not be moved to a different hutch, unless its hutch is exposed to the weather, when it will do better in a smaller, warmer hutch. The moult process can be helped by hand-grooming the rabbit, and also by giving a little linseed jelly in the mash feed several times a week.

The best way to do this is to use a tablespoonful of linseed to a pint of water, bring it to the boil, and then let it simmer gently until it turns to jelly. Add about half a teaspoonful of this to the mash feed every other day until the old coat has been shed.

Sometimes the moult begins at the tail and works forward, sometimes at the head and works backwards. Rabbits should not show bare patches even when moulting, because as the old coat is shed, the new one should have grown up underneath it. The losing of one coat and the growing of another imposes a certain strain on the rabbit, and while it is not ill, it needs a little extra care and good feeding at this time. It is unwise to breed from moulting rabbits, particularly does; they need all their energies for the growth of a new coat, and the added strain of producing or rearing a litter is not advisable.

Caponisation.—Caponisation or castration is seldom worth while in rabbits, as it has very few advantages. One reason for doing it is to prevent bucks in colonies from fighting, but if the bucks are being kept only for table purposes, it is best to use them before they reach that stage. If the animals are being bred for pelts, they should in any case be housed in separate hutches before reaching the fighting stage. Caponisation is inclined to make rabbits lazy, and this retards the fur growth so that they never appear to be in prime fur.

Rabbit manure as a fertiliser.—Well-rotted rabbit manure is of higher value than farmyard manure, so the rabbit breeder should make full use of it. When fresh rabbit manure was analysed it was found to be richer in nitrogen, phosphoric acid and potash than farmyard manure, and to resemble closely the rich poultry manure. It is better to use rabbit manure when it has been well rotted, so the hutch cleanings should be heaped up and watered when necessary. By applying small amounts of water at regular intervals the heap is kept in a condition in which it can heat or ferment. By doing this the manure can be made ready for use within a few weeks. Heating the manure in this way has two advantages, it kills any weed seeds that may be in it, and it makes it ready for use in a short time, before it has lost any of its fertilising qualities.

If the litter from the hutches contains sawdust, or anything that may be considered injurious to the soil, it should be burnt, if possible on the ground intended for cultivation. The ash from the burnt manure has a high value as a fertiliser.

Ground that is well dressed with rabbit manure should be limed periodically in order to get the best results. The rabbit manure should not be used too thickly, about a barrow load to ten square yards is quite a good amount, and if the ground has been well manured in recent years, less will be quite satisfactory.

CHAPTER 6

BREEDING

BREEDING stock must always be strong, lively, healthy rabbits and they must be free from moult. Breeding from stock obviously not at their best, or suffering from moult, is asking for trouble among the youngsters when they are born.

Rabbits must be mature before being bred from. The use of immature breeding stock means that the litters will lack stamina, and the parents will never make up for the check in growth caused by early breeding. Rabbits mature at different ages, according to the size of the variety. Small breeds, like the Polish and Dutch, are often fully mature at six months; medium breeds such as the Chinchilla, Sables and Rex, mature at from seven to eight months, and big breeds, like the Flemish and Chinchilla Giganta, should not be bred from until they are eight to nine months old.

Although it is sometimes stated that a doe is almost always ready to accept service, it is a fact that wild rabbits rarely breed through the winter months. The ovaries seem to remain quiescent through the cold weather. This does not apply in equal measure to the tame rabbit, which can be bred from at any period of the year, provided the hutches are warm, and the animals are well fed, but not too fat. Over-fatness is one of the most frequent causes of unfertile matings because the breeding organs are amongst the first to lay on fat, and this makes the doe sterile.

The doe which is willing to be mated usually shows a purplish and rather congested sexual organ. If the sexual organ looks dry and pale, it is a sign that the doe is not 'in season.' Other signs that a doe is anxious to be mated are restlessness, and stamping on the hutch floor. Some does will carry hay about as though to make a nest, or even begin to pluck themselves. If a doe is mated immediately she begins to show such signs, the mating is nearly always successful. On the other hand, a doe may show none of the obvious signs of wishing to mate, and yet mate readily and with successful results.

If possible choose a warm, sunny day for mating stock. Does will often refuse to mate on a bad day, especially if there is a cold wind. For the actual mating, always put the doe into the buck's hutch. Never reverse the procedure, because does are often resentful of a buck being put in with them, and may turn on him and savage him before he can be removed. If the doe is willing to be mated, she will at once lie in the correct position, and raise her hindquarters. If she is not anxious to mate, she may refuse to raise her hindquarters and tail at first, but after a few minutes of courtship by the buck, she will assume the correct attitude. If she refuses in spite of the buck's efforts, and remains crouched in the corner of the hutch, it is best to remove her, and try again on another occasion.

On completion of the mating, the buck will usually fall over on its side, and the fall being backwards or sideways. The doe should be removed as soon as the mating has been accomplished. There is no point in allowing a second or third mating, and this is probably what will happen if the two rabbits are left together in the hutch for any length of time. The male produces millions of spermatoza at a single ejaculation, while only a limited number of ova are sufficiently ripe to be discharged from the ovaries of the doe. It is the number of ova which control the size of the litter, although litter size is indirectly controlled by the male as this is definitely an inherited character.

Does which are difficult to mate can sometimes be brought into season by feeding a few sprays of flowering groundsel, or some sprays of parsley. If this fails, soak a few maple peas (these are found in pigeon corn) until they begin to sprout, and add three or four to the ordinary food for a few days.

Another way of bringing a difficult doe into season is to put her into a hutch previously occupied by a buck, and leave her there for a day or two. Do not clean the hutch out first.

Mated does need no special treatment, but they do not want to be handled too much, and towards the end of their pregnancy sudden unusual noises are bad for them.

It is not always easy to tell if a doe is in-kindle except towards the end of the time. The gestation period is approximately thirty-one days, but thirty days or thirty-two days is no uncommon time. The shortest gestation period known to have produced live youngsters is twenty-six days, though there are several instances of does which kindled many days later than the usual period.

Pregnant does should be well fed. They do not need to be fattened, but should have the usual amount of good mash containing the best of the house-scraps available. In addition they should have plenty of succulent food to help in forming a good milk supply. Carrots are the best of the root crops for pregnant and nursing does, though others are satisfactory. Pregnant does should have the pick of the greenfood available and should always be given water, or milk and water, to drink.

It is best to use a nest box, particularly if the litter is born early in the year when the weather is cold. This should be put in about a week before the doe is due to kindle, so that she has plenty of time to get used to it. She should also be given a good supply of soft hay for nest-making purposes. Rough hay will do, but straw is unsuitable, it is too stiff and hard to be suitable for nest-making. The nest box can be filled with hay when it is put in the hutch.

Any wooden box, about eighteen inches long by ten inches wide and five or six inches high will do. A big breed will naturally need a rather bigger box. One side can be lowered a little to allow the doe to get in and out with ease. If a few small holes are bored in the bottom of the box, and two pieces of wood nailed along the bottom to raise it from the ground, this will keep the bottom of the box from becoming damp.

Some does will make their nest behind the nesting box, or even in the opposite corner of the hutch. If this happens a few days before the doe is due to kindle, the nest can be picked up and put in the box, having first put the box in the place where the nest was made. If the doe still refuses to make her nest in the box, it is best to leave her alone.

The doe will line her nest with fur which she plucks from her chest and flanks. It is quite a good plan to keep a 'fluff box' into which any surplus nest-lining can be placed, so that if a doe does not make a nest, some of this spare fur can be used to keep the youngsters warm until the doe attends to this matter herself.

It is quite usual for a doe to go off her feed a day or so before she is due to kindle, and for her droppings to be rather soft. This is quite normal and nothing to be worried about. Does are always very thirsty at kindling time and a doe due to kindle must have plenty of drinking water. Lack of drinking water at kindling time is a frequent cause of does eating their young. Does need no help when they are kindling and are far better if left alone. It is always possible to tell when a doe has kindled, both by her appearance and by looking at the nest where the movements of the young rabbits can usually be discerned.

It is advisable to look at the babies when they are a day old, but the doe should be removed from the hutch while this is being done, otherwise she may be upset. If she is put into a spare hutch and given a tit-bit of greenfood or roots to keep her occupied, she need never know the nest has been disturbed.

Rub the hands well in the hutch litter before touching the nest, so that no strange smells upset the doe when she returns. Open the nest carefully at the top, and examine the youngsters as quickly as possible. Baby rabbits are born blind, and with very little fur, so that they quickly become chilled. If there is a dead youngster, or one which is obviously puny, remove it at once.

A doe should not be left with more than six or seven youngsters if she is to feed them well, and rear healthy, robust youngsters. If two does are mated at the same time, it is often possible to foster youngsters from an over-large litter to a litter which is smaller. If no foster-mother is available, it is usually best to keep more does than bucks, unless, of course, it is possible to tell at this early stage which are the best looking of any particular breed. At about a day old, baby does can be distinguished from young bucks, because of the teats which show as tiny white marks on each side of the belly. Once the fur begins to grow, these marks are no longer discernable.

If you have two does kindling at the same time, and want to foster the young of one doe, it should be done in much the same way as one examines a nest of youngsters. Fostering can be done up to four days after birth, and in some cases has been done successfully even later, but the safest time is when the young rabbits are about twenty-four hours old. There should not be more than two days' difference in age of the litters that are to be mixed, otherwise the doe may detect the difference.

Both does should be taken from their hutches, and housed separately with some food to keep them busy. Take the surplus youngsters from the large litter and put them in a box filled with warm material or cotton wool. Keep them covered otherwise they will get chilled. Cover up the youngsters left behind, then put those in the box into their new home, covering them well.

It is advisable to leave the foster-mother out of the hutch for a short while, until the newly-introduced babies thoroughly absorb the smell of the nest.

Record any changes of litters on the hutch cards. By having two or more does to kindle at the same time, it often means that youngsters from large litters which would have to be destroyed, can be saved and reared and wastage prevented.

Once the litter has been examined and everything necessary has been done, it is not advisable to disturb the nest again. The doe will do all that is necessary in feeding and caring for the youngsters, though she will not often be seen feeding them.

If the weather turns colder while the youngsters are in the nest, it is a good plan to put a little extra hay into the nesting compartment in case the doe wants to add to the nest.

If there is no suitable nesting material, the doe may pile wet litter, or even food and water dishes on the nest in an effort to keep the young rabbits warm.

The young rabbits will open their eyes when they are about ten days old, but they will not leave the nest until they are about three weeks old. If they come out much earlier than this, it means that they are not getting sufficient milk from the doe, and have been driven out because they are hungry. To prevent this, nursing does should be given ample supplies of succulent food, particularly greenfoods. When the young rabbits leave the nest and begin to nibble at the food in the hutch, it is almost always greenfood they eat first. If the doe has had plenty of greens, the young rabbits will not be upset by their first meal of solid greenstuff.

It is as well to see that the young rabbits are healthy and free from any defects or deformities when they leave the nest. Sometimes their eyes fail to open completely by the time they leave the nest, due to colds or eye infection, and they need to be gently bathed with tepid water, and a little golden eye ointment applied.

Once the young rabbits leave the nest, particular care must be taken to see that the food is fresh, of good quality, and that it does not become soiled. The quantities of food given will now need to be increased almost daily, and any sudden changes of diet must be avoided, otherwise the youngsters may get digestive troubles, and suffer a check in growth.

The young rabbits should remain with the doe for about six weeks during summer weather, and seven weeks during winter. At the end of this time, it is best to remove the doe to a new hutch, and to leave the youngsters where they are for a week or ten days. This allows them to become used to doing without their mother before they have to be parted from each other and get used to the new hutch. All these things at once prove a big strain on youngsters, and weaning can prove a critical time unless handled with care.

At the end of a week or ten days, the young rabbits can be put into other hutches in batches according to the size of the hutch, or can be put into indoor colonies, or Morant hutches outside if the weather is good.

The doe will need a rest of about a fortnight after the youngsters are weaned. If she does not seem in good condition at the end of this time, she should be given longer. Does vary a good deal in condition after suckling a litter, but should never be re-mated until they are perfectly fit.

If a doe loses her litter at birth, she can be re-mated almost at once. It is rearing a litter, not actually producing them, which is the greater strain on the doe.

Pseudo-pregnancy.—This state of pseudo-pregnancy, or false pregnancy, occurs fairly frequently in rabbits. The doe mates quite readily, and appears to be pregnant, but in fact will produce no litter, because conception has not taken place. The doe may commence to make her nest, and her milk glands will begin to swell at about the eighteenth day after mating. This early nest-making, when the doe carries hay about in her mouth, and begins to pluck herself less than three weeks after mating, is almost always a sign of pseudo-pregnancy. When this occurs the doe should be mated again immediately. She will accept service readily at such a time, and the matings are frequently successful. Even if she should prove to be truly pregnant, such a mating will do no harm, and if it was, as is most probably the case, a false pregnancy, valuable time will have been saved.

Scattered litters.—If a doe scatters her youngsters over the hutch floor, and seems to take no interest in them, it is sometimes possible to save them if they can be found before they get too chilled. They should be put in a box lined with some warm material and put in a warm room fairly near the fire. They can do without food for twenty-four hours, but they cannot do without warmth. The cause of a doe neglecting her young is often because her milk supply has not begun to function. If the milk comes within a few hours of the birth of the litter, as it frequently does, the youngsters can be returned to the nest and the doe will soon begin to look after them. Maiden does are more likely to scatter their youngsters than experienced does.

If a doe dies, it is possible to rear orphaned babies from quite an early age by hand-feeding if one has the time to do it. Make a mixture of two parts cow's milk and one part water, and warm until the chill is taken off. Feed the youngsters by means of a fountain pen filler. A piece of bicycle valve tubing on the end of the filler makes it easier for the young rabbits to suck and does away with the danger of biting off the end of the filler. The young rabbit will suck in the normal way, and will take one or two fillers' full to begin with, but the amount should be increased almost daily. At first the youngsters should be fed every three hours during the day. They must be kept indoors in a warm room, in a box or similar receptacle, and should be lightly but warmly covered with soft woollen material or soft hay. When the youngsters are about three weeks old, they can have bread and milk from a saucer and some soft, good quality hay.

Three litters a year, and possibly four if the doe is in excellent condition, are all that should be expected from a doe. To try to get more litters than this means that the doe will have no time to recover from one litter before being mated again, and the result will be weak litters that will not thrive and will be very prone to disease.

There is a belief among some rabbit-breeders that if a doe has been mated to a buck of another breed, and produces a cross-bred litter, she will be spoilt for true breeding purposes. This is not so. Each mating affects only the litter born as a direct result of it and has no effect whatever on subsequent matings and litters. If a pure-bred doe has been mated to a buck of another breed, and produced a cross-bred litter, she will still breed true when she is mated to a buck of her own breed.

CHAPTER 7

REARING YOUNG STOCK

THE period immediately after weaning is a critical one in the life of young rabbits. Unless they get careful attention at this time, losses among weaned litters may be heavy. They must be carefully fed, and the diet must be the same as that given while the doe was with them. Common mistakes with newly-weaned youngsters are overcrowding and wrong feeding.

It is vital that the young rabbits should be kept growing. A check in growth at this stage is very rarely made up later on. Attacks of scours and digestive upsets will check growth, but both of these can be avoided. There should be no sudden changes in feeding, and as young rabbits are somewhat greedy feeders, it is a good plan to give them mash or hay before giving greenfood, so that they can take the edge off their appetites before tackling the succulent greenfood.

Young rabbits should have at least three meals daily. If they go for long periods without food, they eat far too rapidly when they are fed, and this sets up digestive troubles. At this stage the stomach juices cannot deal with large masses of food, with the result that it begins to decompose in the stomach, and violent indigestion and scours result. Either of these can be fatal where young rabbits are concerned.

A wide variation of food is necessary to ensure that the young rabbits get all the necessary proteins, vitamins and minerals. It is difficult to satisfy the appetites of young rabbits at this stage, so the best way of making sure they get enough is to give sufficient food so that traces of it are left by the next mealtime.

To find out whether a litter is progressing satisfactorily, it is a good plan to weigh individual youngsters now and again. An easy method of calculating the approximate weight of young rabbits is to allow one pound body weight for every four weeks of growth. This does not apply to small breeds, like the Polish and Dutch, nor to very big ones, like the Flemish, but is a fairly accurate standard for the medium breeds. If the litter is small, some of the weaned rabbits may weigh considerably more than two pounds at two months old, while if the litter is big and has not been reduced, they may weigh less.

By weighing the youngsters occasionally it is possible to discover if they are making the right progress. If there is a small rabbit among the litter, which gains little weight, it may be suffering from coccidiosis, and it is often better to destroy such a rabbit at once, rather than risk an outbreak of infection among the others.

Once the young rabbits have become used to feeding on their own, and doing without the doe, they can either be penned in pairs in ordinary hutches, or if preferred, they can be kept in colonies or pens. This is a labour-saving way of rearing youngsters, and if a shed or outhouse is available for use in this way, it saves a good many hutches.

It is a fairly simple matter to divide up the space by means of wire netting and wood battens. It is quite a good plan to sex the youngsters before they are put into colonies, then colonies of does and colonies of bucks can be made up. There is no reason why the young rabbits from different litters should not be mixed if they are approximately the same age. Colonies of bucks and does together can be made, but the bucks must be removed when they are between fourteen and sixteen weeks old, otherwise they will mature too early, and develop objectionable habits. For this reason most breeders prefer to separate the sexes when the colonies are first made up.

In making a colony run for a number of weaned rabbits, allow two square feet as the minimum amount of floor space for each rabbit. However many rabbits you have, it is not advisable to run more than twenty-five rabbits in a colony pen.

In good weather young rabbits can be reared in Morant hutches out of doors. They need part of the hutch covered in to give them shelter from sun and rain. Youngsters thrive well when housed in colonies, perhaps because of the extra opportunities it gives for exercise.

The sex of a young rabbit can be decided quite easily, even

though in young bucks the testes are not clearly discernible. Place the rabbit on its back on a table or box, using one hand to hold it still, and the thumb and forefinger of the other hand to manipulate the sexual organs. Press gently on the organ so that it protrudes a little. The male organ is shaped like a cylinder, but the female organ is oval and has a V-shaped opening. The female organ will not protrude so far as the organ of the male. The examination should be completed as quickly as possible, and the pressure exerted should be very gentle.

If young rabbits are intended for show purposes, they should certainly be ringed. Many breeders like to ring almost all their young stock, except perhaps those obviously destined for the pot. Rings can be obtained in seven different sizes as follows:

Size A—Polish.

Size B—Argentè Bleu, Argentè Crème, Dutch, Himalaya, Nubian and Tan.

Size C—Silvers, Argentè Brun.

Size D—Argentè de Champagne, Beaver Chifox, Chinchilla, English, Lilac, Sable, Fox, Havana, Siberian, Smoke Pearl, Squirrel.

Size E—Angora, Harlequin, New Zealand Red, Rex Breeds.

Size F—Beveren Belgian, Lop, Chinchilla Giganta.

Size G—Flemish Giant.

The breed of rabbit for which the rings are required should always be stated when ordering.

Rabbits should have their rings fitted between the age of eight and twelve weeks. It is not advisable to ring earlier than this or the rings may slip off. To ring a young rabbit, hold it gently but firmly beneath the left arm, stretch out one hind leg, put the ring carefully over the foot and push it gently up the leg until it is over the hock joint. It is then in position and will not slip off again. It does not matter which leg the ring goes on. Some breeders put does' rings on the right leg and bucks' on the left, but this is a matter of choice.

If rabbits become mixed at shows, it is a comparatively simple matter to correct any mistakes if all the exhibits are ringed.

If you buy or sell a ringed rabbit, you should take steps to have the ring number transferred. A small fee is charged for the registration of each transfer, and transfer cards may be obtained from the same source as the rings.

If rabbits need to be marked in some way, and their owner does not want the expense of ringing them, they can be marked with an indelible pencil on the inside of the ear or they can be tattooed. To tattoo a rabbit's ear, it should be placed on a flat piece of wood, and a number or other mark of indentification pricked on the thin part of the ear. Smear this quickly with marking ink and it will give a clear and lasting mark.

The age of a young rabbit can be determined fairly accurately by the progress of the intermediate moult. This is shown by a very clear line on the face between the flossy new fur and the dull looking old fur. This line advances steadily as moult proceeds. At about six weeks it can be seen just above the nose and by the time the rabbit is eight weeks old, it is half-way between the eyes and the nose.

By the tenth week the whole face has usually moulted, and the moult line is wedge-shaped, and extends from above the ears on either side to a point between the eyes across the nose. By three months the lower end of the wedge is practically clear of the eyes, and by the time the young rabbit is four months old, the face has completely moulted, and all that remains of the baby coat is a small wedge-shaped patch between the ears.

CHAPTER 8

MANAGEMENT OF PELT RABBITS

THE raising of rabbits for their pelts as well as for carcases is one of the most profitable forms of rabbit keeping, but the pelts must be taken at the right time, and the rabbits well fed and housed if the best results are to be obtained.

Rabbits which are required for producing prime pelts should be housed in single hutches from the age of 4½ months onward. If they are allowed to run together after this the pelts may be damaged through fighting or play, or may become hutch stained.

Fur rabbits should also be kept out of very strong sunlight, as this makes the fur go rusty, or fades the colour, and gives the pelt a rather dry and brittle appearance. This does not mean that pelt rabbits must be kept in the dark. This will not allow them to grow into healthy adults, and if a rabbit is not in good health its pelt will lack the density and sheen that is the mark of a first class pelt. Pelt rabbits should have fairly sheltered hutches, and the fronts should be shaded when the sunlight is very strong.

It is usually the rabbits born from the beginning of March until August which show the best profits as pelt rabbits, because these come into prime pelt from November until March, which is the best time of year for producing dense, moult free pelts. Pelt rabbits must be kept longer than those which are for carcase production only, thus costing more to feed, so it is very important that the pelt should be taken at the right time.

Rabbits come into prime coat from about six and a half months of age and onward. If they come into adult coat during the summer, they begin to moult again almost immediately, because of the heat, and a summer pelt never has the thickness and quality of a winter one.

There is a stage at about four and a half months, when a rabbit has a good tight coat for a short period, and if pelt rabbits can be killed just at this time, the pelt will be worth dressing, although it will not be really prime. Pelts taken at this stage are known as intermediate pelts. The Chinchilla rabbit produces quite a good pelt at this stage and is a good breed to keep for those who want to produce a quantity of meat rabbits to kill off at a fairly early stage.

For the production of intermediate pelts the normal furred varieties are a better proposition than the Rex breeds, which sometimes tend to have a rather sparse coat at this stage.

Pelt rabbits should be given plenty of litter in their hutches as this soaks up the urine, and reduces the risk of the pelt becoming hutch stained. If the rabbits are white, or pale coloured, it is best to limewash the insides of the hutches, rather than to creosote them, though creosote is quite suitable for darker coated rabbits.

The type of feeding can also have a marked effect on the production of good pelts. If the mash is poor in quality, or dry bran is fed, it will have the effect of making the coat dry and harsh to the touch, instead of soft and silky. Two or three drops of cod liver oil added to the mash every day helps to give a lustre and a sheen to the fur.

There is no need to add minerals to the mash to help fur growth. A good variety of green food will give the rabbits the minerals they need in the right proportions. Sometimes when mineral mixtures are given a rabbit may get too much of one particular kind, and this may have the effect of checking the growth of the pelt rather than encouraging it. A little linseed jelly added to the mash is a help in the production of a good pelt, particularly if given at moulting time.

Pelt rabbits should have water to drink. Some breeders supply the rabbits with a small lump of rock salt, so that if their diet is deficient in salt they can lick it if they want to.

Roots have not the high mineral content that fresh green food has, so when roots are being used, the addition of a little cod liver oil to the mash is more important than when green food is used.

Some rabbits seem to have a harsh, rather coarse coat. These should be crossed with a rabbit of the same breed with a finer textured coat. Similarly, rabbits whose pelts lack density should be crossed with those having very dense pelts, and if length is required cross rabbits failing in this respect with longer coated rabbits.

Pelt rabbits must be killed when they are in really prime coat. If they are killed while they are still moulting, either when they are just completing one moult, or just beginning another, it means that the pelt is of very little value. Moult patches on the pelt show on the skin side as blue black marks. The hair on the skin above these patches is loose and when the pelt is cured, it is likely to fall out, leaving a bare place.

It can be seen quite easily whether a rabbit is likely to be ready for pelting. Obvious signs of moult and loose hairs means that the rabbit has not reached the prime pelt stage. A rabbit ready for pelting should look sleek, and there should be no sign of moult to the casual glance. When rabbits look like this, each one needs a careful and thorough examination to make sure that it is in fact, free from moult.

The rabbit should be placed on a table, or held with the left hand supporting the weight. Blow the fur apart until the skin can be seen. This should appear flesh coloured. If blue black patches are seen when the fur is blown apart this means that the moult is not complete at that spot. Patches of fur which are shorter than the rest also mean that the new coat is not fully grown, and that the rabbit is not yet in prime pelt.

The parts of a rabbit's body which need particular attention are the flanks, the neck, and the area round the tail. These are the places where the moult usually finishes, and the most likely spots to find moult marks on a rabbit which appears to be in prime coat.

A really prime coat must show no black marks on the skin side when it is killed. Pelts with moult patches can never be relied on to wear well, even if the fur does not come out when the pelt is being dressed.

Rabbits which have not been housed separately, but have run together until they were mature, frequently have these moult marks showing. This is where the pelt has been damaged by pieces being pulled out, and new hairs are growing in the damaged part. If these rabbits have reached the age of prime pelts, it is often not worth keeping them until the pelt clears, because this may take a very long time.

With pelt rabbits it is important to kill them as soon as the pelt is prime. Otherwise they may begin to moult again, and that would mean a very long wait before they came into tight coat once more.

Fashion designers in England are becoming more interested in the finer types of rabbit fur for trimming coats and for making into garments. If a breeder wants to do well with pelts he must breed the kind of furs the buyers want. Two breeds which are always popular are the Chinchilla-rex, which cannot be imitated by dyed skins, and closely resembles real Chinchilla, and the Havana-rex, a good deep brown colour which is always popular. The Siamese-rex, which can be made up to imitate phantom beaver, is another popular choice with the fur buyers.

The pelt buyers complain that far too many of the pelts they are offered are spoiled by being hutch stained. This can be prevented by seeing that hutches are well drained, and bedding plentiful, particularly when the rabbits are getting a lot of green food or roots which cause extra urine in the hutches.

When choosing breeding stock from among the pelt rabbits, the intermediate coat will give some idea as to what the adult coat will be, and points for consideration among young stock chosen for breeders are colour texture, and density of fur. One of the furriers' chief requirements is good density of fur right down to the skin. The density must also be even—the entire pelt must be dense, not only parts of it. This even and uniform density can never be bred into a strain except by using breeding stock whose coats are themselves of the required density.

Good colour is, of course, another important factor to consider in the choice of breeding stock, and the colour must be even and free from patchiness.

CHAPTER 9

KILLING AND PELTING

FEW people like killing rabbits, and many fight shy of it alto-gether, yet if it is done properly, it is quite easy to do, and is humane, causing the rabbit neither distress nor pain. Rabbits which are to be killed should not have had any food for twelve hours previous to killing. This makes the carcase easier to deal with when skinning and paunching. For this reason it is better to kill rabbits in the morning after they have had a normal fast during the night.

Experienced breeders can kill rabbits by dislocating the neck, but this is not the easiest method for the beginner. Novices would do better to kill their rabbits in the following way. Put the rabbit on a box or table where it will sit quietly. With the left hand hold the rabbit's ears slightly forward, and with the right, using a short heavy stick, give the animal a sharp blow at the base of the ears. This will kill the rabbit immediately, and it should fall on its side. It may kick a little after falling, but this is only the reflex action of the nerves. Only one blow should be necessary. Many people can kill a rabbit without using a stick, but by using the side of their hand to strike the blow.

For the more experienced breeder, dislocation of the neck is the best method of killing. Taking the rabbit by the hind legs in the right hand, take the back of the head in the left hand, stretch the rabbit out straight and with the rabbit's head held back, a quick jerk of the left hand will break its neck. It is important to keep the rabbit's body fully stretched until its neck has been broken.

When the rabbit has been killed, it should be hung by the hind legs for about five minutes to allow the blood to drain down to the head. If this is not done, the rabbit's flesh will be dark in appearance, and the blood may make skinning difficult. To make the flesh very white, like chicken, the rabbit needs to be bled. To do this, stick a very sharp knife, or a stiletto, through the roof of the mouth, and let the blood drain away into a receptacle.

Rabbits should be skinned or pelted fairly soon after killing, because it is easier to remove the pelt before the carcase becomes stiff and set. Hang the rabbit by a string tied to one hind leg at a convenient height to work. Have ready a sharp, pointed knife, and a soft cloth on which to wipe the hands if they become blood-stained. Insert the knife at the hock-joint on the back leg, and cut down to the vent on the inside of the leg; then from the vent up to the hock-joint on the other leg. Cut off the tail, or pull it out, and set each hind leg free from the pelt.

Having done this, the skin can by pulled down over the body like turning a sleeve inside out. If the skin clings tightly in any particular place, use the knife to set it free. In older rabbits the ligaments are sometimes tough, and this makes the use of the knife necessary, but with the majority of rabbits the skin pulls down over the body very easily.

When the front legs are reached, these should be set free from the pelt and severed at the hocks. The skin should be pulled off, still sleeve-fashion, until the ears are reached. The ears must be severed at the base, and then the skin can be pulled off down to the nose. The head is usually the hardest part to skin, and the knife will be needed to cut the skin round the eyes and nose. This part of the pelt is of no use, so it does not matter if it is damaged in removing it from the carcase, but the head must be skinned clean if the carcase is to be offered for sale.

As soon as the pelt has been removed, the rabbit should be paunched. This is done by making a slit down the belly from the vent to the breast-bone. Use the knife lightly so that it only cuts through the skin, and does not break any of the intestines, otherwise the paunching will be unnecessarily messy. When the slit is made the entrails will fall forward. The liver and the kidneys must not be removed, but the remainder can all be removed with the left hand, while the right hand is used to sever the gut where the paunch joins the liver.

The gall bladder, a small greenish-black bag found fairly high on the liver, must be removed carefully. This contains the bitter gall fluid, and if it is broken in being removed, or is not removed before the rabbit is cooked, it will taint the flesh.

The hind legs should be forced apart and the pelvic joint split through, so that the last piece of gut and any excreta it contains may be removed. Some carcase buyers do not want the pelvic bone split, but prefer breeders to remove the piece of gut without splitting the bone. This can be done fairly easily by pulling the gut through from above the vent.

Rabbit carcases should never be washed, as this will make them less easy to keep and will spoil the appearance of the flesh. If they become stained during the skinning and paunching operations, wipe them with a soft dry cloth.

Carcases should be allowed to remain hanging in a cool place for about twelve hours, until they become stiff. They must never be hung in direct sunshine, or in wind, as this will discolour the flesh.

If the carcase is to be dressed Ostend fashion, the fore paws should be cut of at the joint. and the ends of the legs tucked in small insertions made between the ribs. The hind feet should be cut off to within an inch of the joint, and a hole should be cut between the sinew and the leg on one leg, so that the other leg can be threaded through.

Carcase Proportions.—The proportion of live weight to the dressed carcase depends on the breed of rabbit, its age, and the way it has been fed. A good many rabbits dress out at something over sixty per cent. of the live weight when skinned and paunched. Younger rabbits do not dress as well in proportion to their live weight. A young rabbit which weighs between 2 lb. and $2\frac{1}{2}$ lb. often dresses out at no more than $1\frac{1}{2}$ lb. Such carcases are as a general rule too small for usual requirements, but young rabbits of this age are sometimes used for frying, particularly in the United States.

By four months the live weight of an average sized rabbit should be about 4 lb., and when skinned and dressed provides a carcase a little over two pounds. While the loss of weight is not so high as in younger rabbits it is still too high to make it economic to kill rabbits at this age. After the age of four months sex shows some small effect on the proportions, and rabbits weighing about 5 lb. produce carcases between 2¾ lb. and 3 lb. with does weighing a little more than bucks.

On an average the best time for killing a rabbit for table, provided it has developed properly, is five months old. Many people kill them a little earlier, but in the period of from four to five months, the average rabbit, fed on present day rations, puts on weight more rapidly than at any other period, so the extra cost in feeding for a couple of weeks longer, is justified.

The place where a rabbit carries most meat is on the back and thighs. Table rabbits should be compact and cobby, with a broad back and well developed hind legs.

Carcases should not be packed for despatch until they are set. They should be packed in a hamper or box lined with greaseproof paper. Rabbit carcases travel better if packed in bulk in a box lined with greaseproof than they do if each carcase is separately wrapped.

The pelt of the rabbit will need attention as soon as it is removed from the rabbit. It should not be left to lie in a heap for hours after its removal, otherwise it may become heated, and if this happens, it will soon begin to decompose. It should be opened up by cutting from the vent down the centre of the belly to the throat. Use a very sharp knife or a razor blade and take care that the pelt is being cut down the belly, and not down the back, as the back is the most valuable part of the pelt.

Skins must be properly dried before they are stored and also before they are sent away for dressing. Some firms accept wet pelts, but there is always a risk that the pelts will decompose or become stained in transit, and it is quite simple, and much more satisfactory, to dry them first.

The best way to dry a skin is to nail it on to a board, which should measure about thirty inches long and eighteen inches wide. A door, or a box, will do for nailing out pelts, but drying boards are quite simple to make from odd pieces of wood.

The skin should be placed on the board, fur side down, and nailed out in a good rectangular shape. It is easier to put a tack in each corner first, and pull the pelt to its fullest extent, but do not over-stretch. A pelt from a medium-sized rabbit should be from seventeen to eighteen inches long, and about fourteen inches wide. When the tacks are in the four corners, tack along each side, using as many tacks as are necessary to get the skin nailed out flat and smooth. Place the tacks as near the edge of the pelt as possible, so that the main part of it is not marked by tack holes.

The board with the tacked skin should be hung in an airy shed, or a warm room, and left until the skin is quite dry and stiff. In good weather this will only take four or five days, but in bad weather it may be up to ten days before the pelt is really dry. Never put a pelt in front of a fire, or similar direct heat, to hurry the drying process. Skins which are dried rapidly in this way are almost useless. They are thin and papery when dressed, and are known to the trade as 'burnts'.

Air is necessary, as well as some warmth, so that a closed space like an airing cupboard will not give good results. In summer weather the pelts should not be exposed to strong sunlight. They will dry quickly enough in a shady spot where there is plenty of air. During hot weather pelts need watching in case blow flies lay their eggs in them. Under the pieces of fat which adhere to the skin, or where the pelt curls a little at the edges, are favourite spots for blow flies to lay eggs. If these are allowed to hatch, the maggots will soon spoil the pelt.

Hang the pelt where it cannot be attacked by vermin. They will sometimes spoil a pelt by trying to gnaw the fat off.

When the pelts are partly dry, and the fat has set hard, it can be removed by scraping with a blunt knife. Only remove the fat, do not scrape away the tissue or natural skin on the inside of the pelt. Some of this will have to be removed later, to make the pelt supple, but it is a skilled process and should be left to the pelt-dresser.

If this fat is not removed, it will cause the pelt to putrefy and make the part of skin underneath the fat useless for dressing. Some people make the mistake of leaving the tail on the pelt. This, too, has a good deal of flesh and fat, and begins to putrefy before it can dry out. This rotting process will spread up the pelt if it is not checked, so the tail should always be removed.

When the pelts are absolutely dry and stiff, they should be

removed from the boards for storing. If there is any doubt at all as to whether the pelt is completely dry, leave it for a further day or two. Skins not thoroughly dried will damp-off unless the weather is very dry and hot, and will begin to decompose.

Before storing the pelts see that all the nails are removed. If nails are left in when the pelts are sent for dressing, they may do serious damage to the pelt-dressing machinery, and may also tear holes in other people's pelts.

The pelts should be stored by packing fur to fur, or skin to skin. If the skin of one pelt is placed on the fur of another, it may cause it to become greasy or stained.

Pelts are liable to be attacked by moth and other insects, so they should always be stored in an air-tight box. It is a wise precaution to wrap each pair of pelts in newspaper, and to put some flaked naphthaline among the papers. Moth balls are not as good as the many mothicides which can be obtained nowadays which kill moths and larva. Ordinary moth balls do not kill either, they merely discourage the moths and even in this respect are not always successful.

When sending the pelts to the dressers for processing, it is best to wait until a dozen pelts are ready, because most firms charge a cheaper rate if a dozen pelts are sent at once. If the pelts are to be sold in the air-dried state, try to match the pelts as far as possible before offering them for sale. Matched pelts always command a higher price than unmatched ones.

When sending pelts through the post it is best to roll them if they cannot be packed flat. Creasing the pelts by folding them may cause permanent damage. Do not let any fur get mixed up with the knot when tying pelts, otherwise this piece of fur may be pulled out when the knot is untied.

The Battery System of Hutches

The Colony System of Hutches

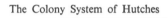

(*above*)
A rabbit shed with shutters for use in winter and a curtain for shade in summer.

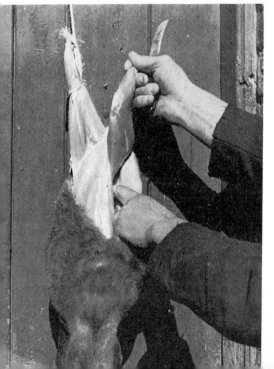

(*left*)
Skinning a rabbit.
Hang up the rabbit and cut out the hind legs first.

CHAPTER 10

PELT DRESSING

IT is not advisable to attempt to cure pelts at home if they are t
be used for coats, capes, gloves or other worth while articles. Th
pelt dressers, who have modern machines at their disposal, ca
make a much better job of it than the home dresser, and also th
actual handling of the skins is a skilled craft which, like all craft
takes a long time to perfect.

Most people, however, get a few poorer quality pelts which ai
perhaps not worth sending to be dressed, or which they feel the
would like to dress themselves. Pelt dressing at home requires
good deal of time and patience if good results are to be achieved

Pelts intended for home dressing should be soaked in sever:
lots of clean, tepid water. Soft water is best if it is availabl
Thick skins will need to be soaked longer than others, but a
types of skin will need soaking for at least three hours. The
must be soft and pliable before they can be treated, but the
must not remain soaking too long, otherwise the hairs will begi
to come out.

It is best to begin on a doe's pelt, as buck pelts, particular
those from older bucks, are very thick skinned, and cons
quently, difficult to dress so that they are soft and easy to handl
These pelts often finish up stiff and hard, in spite of all efforts
soften them.

When the skin is soft, it should be laid over a roller, or roun
ed surface, and the pieces of flesh and fat remaining on it, ai
also a thin layer of tissue; should be removed by working with
blunt knife or a file. The pelt dressers do this by working the sk
over a fixed knife. Until the surplus tissue had been removed, t
skin will not be soft and pliable, but it is important not to r
move too much, and not to tear the skin. The tissue left shou
be of even thickness all over the pelt.

The natural grease and oil must be worked out of the sk

before it can be dressed. To do this rinse the pelt in lukewarm water, and squeeze it gently to get the grease out. Pelts must never be twisted or wrung, but always gently squeezed dry. The dry skin can be gone over with a little petrol to remove any dirt or stains, and is then ready for dressing. There are several methods of dressing pelts. One method which gives quite good results is the chrome-alum treatment. To do this you need 4 ozs. of chrome-alum, 1½ ozs. of washing soda and 8 ozs. of dextrine. Dissolve each of these materials in separate containers, using about 1½ pints of water in each case. To make the tanning liquid, take about a quarter of a pint of each of the three liquids, and add one to another slowly, stirring all the time. Tip half this mixture into a bowl or bucket, with about a quart of water. Immerse the skin in the liquid, work it about for a while, and leave it for three hours, moving the skin about in the tanning liquid occasionally. Then add the remaining half of the tanning liquid and leave the pelt overnight.

By morning the pelt should be tanned, and it will be a bluish colour. It will need to be well washed and soaked for half an hour in chalk and water. It should then be removed, and washed again.

To soften the pelt make up an emulsion by using ½ oz. of liquid soap and ¼ oz. of neat's-foot oil to a pint of hot water. When the liquid is cool, put the pelt in and work it about well. The more the pelt is worked at this stage the better it will be. It can be left in the emulsion for about twelve hours, then washed well under the tap. When it has been thoroughly rinsed, it can be hung in a warm place to dry.

When the skin side is fairly dry, but the fur side still damp, the pelt needs working backwards and forwards over a chair back. As this is done the blue-green colour which the pelt has acquired in tanning will disappear.

Another method which gives good results is the salt-alum method. Dissolve 1 lb. of alum (ammonia or potash alum) in one gallon of water, and 4 ozs. of washing soda and 8 ozs. of common salt in half a gallon of water. Pour the alum solution slowly into the salt and soda solution, stirring vigorously all the time. Using some of this solution, as required, mix it with flour to make a thin paste. It is advisable to mix the flour with a little water first to prevent any lumps. The skin should be tacked out, fur side down on a piece of board. Protect the pelt with a piece of material or newspaper so that none of the fur comes in contact with the paste.

Coat the skin thinly and evenly with the dressing paste. A layer about half an eighth of an inch thick is sufficient. Leave this on for twenty-four hours, then scrape it off and give the pelt another application. Pelts need two or three dressings like this. Thin skins will probably need only two, but a thick skin from a buck will need three. Leave the last application on for three or four days, then scrape it off.

The skin will be found to be rather stiff and hard. It should be worked well in borax water, adding powdered borax at the rate of one ounce to the gallon. Rinse the pelt well in clear water. Every care must be taken to see that every bit of the pickling paste is rinsed out of the pelt. Squeeze the pelt, but do not wring it. Work it in the hands for a while by pulling and stretching it in all directions, then tack it out, flesh side up, and give it a thin coating of grease or oil, and allow to dry. Neat's-foot oil is good for this purpose. When rubbing the oil into the skin, take care that none of it touches the fur.

When the pelt is almost dry, rub it backwards and forwards, skin side down over the edge of a board or over a chair back. The skins need much working of this sort to make them soft and pliable. Much of the success in dressing depends on how much the skin is worked in this way. If the skin side of the pelt is rough, it helps to work it backward and forward over a sandpaper block. If the skins become dry before the working is complete, damp them before working them again.

When the skin has been worked until it is soft all over, it should be put into a receptacle and covered with clean dry hardwood sawdust. The pelt should be worked about in the sawdust, being gently pulled and worked backwards and forwards in all directions. This not only helps to clean the fur, but will add to its lustre.

If pelts go stiff after they have been cured, soak them in clean, cold water, and hang them over a line to dry slowly. At regular intervals while they are drying, manipulate them with your hands, pulling the pelt in all directions. Rubbing the skin side of the pelts gently with pumice stone will also help matters.

CHAPTER 11

ANGORA RABBITS

THE Angora rabbit stands alone in the rabbit world, for there is no other rabbit which resembles it in appearance. Similarly, the production of Angora wool is a distinctive industry, and quite different from that of keeping rabbits for the production of meat, or of meat and pelts. Angora rabbits do not have to be killed for their coats to be made use of, as pelt rabbits do. The rabbits are clipped at regular periods, and are not killed until their wool production begins to diminish. The flesh of Angoras is not considered to be among the best that can be produced by rabbits, and usually has rather yellow fat. Nevertheless, Angora rabbits make a welcome addition to the menu when their life as wool producers is finished.

Angora rabbits may now be had in several attractive colours, including Smoke Angoras, Golden Angoras and Chinchillated Angoras. The white, however, remain by far the most popular.

The Angora is not a very energetic rabbit and for this reason it can thrive in a rather smaller hutch than the fur rabbits. They are somewhat slower in sex development than other rabbits of their size, and can be allowed to run together in colonies until the bucks are five months old. Then the bucks must be separate, but the does can remain in colonies if necessary for the whole of their lives.

In choosing Angora rabbits for wool, choose well fleshed rabbits weighing not less than 6 lb. The tufts found in the tips of the ears and the feet of Angoras are known as 'furnishings,' and rabbits with good 'furnishings' are usually good wool producers.

The point in feeding Angoras is to choose a method which will keep them in good bodily condition, and at the same time give a high wool yield. Fresh green food is important in this respect, and good clover hay also. Angora rabbits should have a mash feed, but they need not be given mash every day, because they tend to put on fat very quickly. When Angoras become over-fat, the wool yield falls off. If they are fed mainly on good green food and hay with a small ration of mash the results are excellent. Health, wool yield and breeding capacity will be better if the rabbits are not allowed to become too fat.

Up to four months of age there is very little risk of Angoras becoming too fat, and at this time plenty of food is necessary for growth and development. Growth slows down after about the fourth month, and the mash can then be slightly reduced. Angoras should have as much green food or roots as they will eat and two or three ounces of hay daily. It is a good plan to tie the hay into a small bundle before feeding—as they are less likely to get it tangled in their coats, if this is done. Greens and hay, if fed regularly from the time the youngsters begin to eat, will not cause digestive troubles.

Some breeders prefer to keep Angora rabbits on wire floored hutches, so that there is less risk of the wool becoming dirty or matted with litter. If they are kept on wire floors, the wire must be kept very clean so that the droppings fall straight through. If the wire is allowed to get clogged and dirty the whole object of wire floors is defeated. Angoras can be kept quite successfully on ordinary wood floors, but the hutches must be kept very clean, and the rabbits bedded on clean wheat straw.

There are two types of Angora rabbit, the one known as the English type which produces wool of a superfine type, and the French type which produces a coarser quality wool less likely to matt. The superfine English wool commands the higher prices, but the rabbits need more care to prevent the wool from becoming matted. Also the superfine wool does not weigh as much as the coarser type, but it is a mistake to buy Angoras with very coarse wool, as the price for this is considerably less than for the medium and fine wools.

There are some very good Angoras which have been produced from crosses of English and French stock, or from purely British stock which produce a technically 'fine' wool which does not matt. The fact that their wool does not matt is due to the fact that each fibre of the wool is rather stronger and thicker than those of the superfine coated Angoras.

To test the resiliency of Angora wool, tightly compress a handful and then open the hand. If the wool is non-matting it should at once spring back to its original position, while the fine wool will remain compressed for a time after the hand has been opened.

Constant grooming should not be necessary except in the case of the superfine wool producers, but all Angoras should be well groomed before being clipped. Clipping should take place about every three months, according to the length of wool required. If the 3-inch staple length of wool is required it will probably need longer between each clip, but for the commercial production of wool, a more frequent clip, even if the wool is shorter, is probably more profitable. Wool grows quickly up to about two inches long, but after that the growth is rather slower, and consequently the wool is much more expensive to produce.

To groom a rabbit before clipping, use a brush. The type of brush with wire bristles set in a rubber cushion is best. Groom the coat downwards, beginning at the shoulder, and taking a little wool at a time. All seeds or pieces of litter should be removed, and all tangles brushed out. If there should be a hard lump of matted wool in any part of the coat, clip this away.

After grooming, make a parting down the middle of the back, and clip the wool along one side of the parting in a straight line. Clip the wool to within about ½-inch of the skin—it is not advisable to clip closer than this. Continue to clip down in lines downwards, until one side is sheared. Place each swathe of wool in a box as it is clipped. The best wool from the back and sides should be kept apart as first quality, the wool from the flanks as second quality, the belly wool third quality, and a separate container should be used for any stained or matted wool.

It is easier to clip when standing on the opposite side of the rabbit to that which is being clipped, and working from rump to neck on the right side, and vice versa on the left side.

Hold up the rabbit's head to clip the chest, and pull the ears forward to clip any wool left on the neck. The rabbit should be turned on its back and held lightly between the knees while its belly and thighs are clipped. When clipping a breeding doe special care must be taken not to injure the teats.

Always use a sharp pair of scissors for clipping; hairdressing scissors are best for this purpose.

Clipped in this way, a good Angora should yield chiefly first grade wool, though there is bound to be a small proportion of short wool from the belly, thighs and neck. A rabbit which yields 12 ozs. of wool per year should be considered satisfactory, though there are strains which will yield more than this. It is a good idea to keep records of all the clips, then a rabbit which is not producing a sufficient quantity of wool can be replaced by a better one.

The period of usefulness of a wool rabbit varies considerably according to the individual rabbit, the strain, and the management. All Angoras should produce a good crop of wool up to two and three years old, and many will remain in full production for five years or even longer.

When clipping Angoras it is always wise to clip all of one sex first, and preferably bucks before does if several are to be done on the same day. Otherwise the smell of the does on the clipping table excites the bucks and makes them restless and difficult to handle.

Wool binding may occur in Angoras as a result of wool being swallowed, if they nibble at their litter. The risk is greatest when the rabbits are in full coat, so they should be cleaned out frequently when their coats are long. If they are given plenty of green food, this acts as roughage, and lessens the tendency of wool to collect in the stomach and cause trouble.

Wool should be marketed as soon as possible after harvesting, as it is inclined to deteriorate if kept in storage too long. The wool buyers will examine and grade each consignment of wool as they receive it, but better prices will be obtained if the wool is provisionally graded when being clipped, as previously suggested. A tin or box should be kept for each grade, and the wool should be put into its right container as it is taken from the rabbits. Good quality wool tends to deteriorate if stored with poor wool, and it is not always easy to separate the grades when they have been stored together, so that a certain amount of waste is unavoidable. All this lowers the price the seller gets, and reduces the profits from his rabbits.

Any clean tin with a lightly fitting lid is suitable for a wool container, and stout paper bags will do for wool of the poorer grades until a sufficient stock of tins can be obtained. If wool has to be stored for a time, say until there is $\frac{1}{2}$ lb. of wool for despatch, make sure that tin lids fit tightly, and that the tins are stored in a dry place. Damp conditions may cause the wool to tangle, and it will also tangle if it is packed too tightly in the container. If the tin lids fit well, and the wool is packed loosely, it should store quite safely. If, by some mischance, a moth gets into the wool, and it is found to contain the eggs or the grubs, the only safe way is to burn it at once. No buyer will accept wool which has any trace of moth in it. The grades of Angora wool are given below:

First Grade.—Length 3 inches or over. The wool must be clean, bright and lustrous, and free from all shorter wool, or pieces of vegetable matter.

Second Grade.—Length 2 to $2\frac{1}{2}$ inches. The wool should be clean and lustrous, and free from any webbed wool or vegetable matter. It should be as free as possible from shorter lengths of wool, though a little short wool is permissible in this grade.

Third Grade.—This grade includes clean, bright wool between 1 and 2 inches in length and a lower standard includes wool which is slightly stained or webbed.

Tangled and Matted Wool.—This includes all wool which is webbed or matted. The wool must not be stained and must be free from all vegetable matter. Clean wool less than 1 inch in length, and clean combings come under this grade.

Soiled.—This is the least valuable wool of all, and this grade comprises wool of any length which is badly stained, or tangled with vegetable matter. It is worth very little.

Plucking.—Angora wool may be harvested by plucking, and some hand spinners will pay considerably more for plucked wool than the prices ruling for clipped wool. The majority of breeders, however, prefer to clip, as plucking has certain disadvantages. It can be done only when the coat is loose, and as this may not occur all over the body at the same time, it may take two or three weeks before the rabbit can be entirely plucked. Plucking takes much longer than clipping, and can only be done when the wool comes away readily with a light pull. If a sharp tug is necessary, that part of the coat is not 'ripe' for plucking and must be left. It is very painful for a rabbit to be plucked if the coat is not ripe for pulling and may even result in tearing the skin.

CHAPTER 12

RABBIT AILMENTS

TAME rabbits are healthy animals and suffer from very few ailments if they are housed and fed properly, but like all animals they are liable to suffer from certain diseases and it is as well for their owners to know the symptoms of these, and how to cure them. Many diseases can be easily cured, particularly if they are detected in the early stages.

Abortion.—Occasionally, does will produce their young a few days before the natural termination of pregnancy. This is most frequently due to the doe having been disturbed by a sudden unusual noise, or being upset by vermin or other animals, or being roughly handled. It is a wise precaution to burn all litter from the hutch of a doe which has aborted, and to isolate her for a few days, as there are occasions when abortion is caused by germs, and in this case it can be passed on to other does. If a doe does not appear to be pulled down, she can be remated a few days after losing her litter, but unless she seems to be in tip-top condition it is wiser to wait for a time.

Abscess.—Sometimes young bucks housed in colonies fight and the resulting wound forms an abscess unless it is well cleansed. Such abscesses must be treated to remove the pus and allow the abscess to drain, otherwise pus will accumulate beneath the skin. Cut the fur away from the site of the wound, and bathe it well until the pus flows freely. Dress with a mild antiseptic, and bathe frequently to keep the wound open until it is quite clean.

Anaemia and Listlessness.—If a rabbit seems listless and anaemic, it should be given plenty of good greenfood, and nourishing mash. If this does not bring about a change for the better, half a teaspoonful of Parrish's food, twice a day, will usually have the desired result.

Baldness.—If a rabbit remains bald after it is about ten days old, this is an inherited defect. Some young Rex are very slow to grow a good coat, but normal furred rabbits should have plenty of fur at this stage. Patches of baldness may be due to mange, or mycotic infection.

Blindness.—Blindness is normal in baby rabbits up to the age of ten days. If the eyes remain closed after this it may be due to sticky eyes and should be treated quickly, otherwise ingrowing eyelashes will add to the trouble. Gently rub a little Golden Eye Ointment along the closed lids, and this should soften the sticky matter, and allow the eyes to open normally.

Blows or Bloat.—Most rabbit keepers get an occasional case of blows, and it is more common in late summer and autumn. Animals of all ages are affected, though it is most common in half grown youngsters. The belly is distended and the animal lies about obviously in distress. The stomach is filled with gas, due to the food fermenting instead of being digested. This trouble can be caused by irregular feeding or by giving too much of any one kind of greenfood. To treat it, reduce the quantity of greenfood by half, and try to use a different type of greens. Feed the rabbit on good hay and a little mash if it will eat, and give it a teaspoonful of bicarbonate of soda in a little warm milk.

Canker.—This is caused by a mite, which is microscopic in size. Canker is not often met with in young rabbits, but is quite common among older ones, particularly the large-eared breeds. The base of the ears appears inflamed, and may have reddish brown scabs. The affected rabbit constantly scratches its ears, which are tender, and feel warm when touched. If the deeper crusts are ulcerated, and contain pus, clean the ears with a swab of cotton wool soaked in a mild antiseptic, such as ten per cent. hydrogen peroxide. Then apply a little sweet oil, such as olive oil to soften the scabs and crusts. Leave this for a time, then gently clean the ears with a swab, removing any crusts that will come away easily. Burn all dressings used. Two or three such dressings at three or four day intervals, should effect a cure.

To keep the ears healthy, a regular weekly dusting of flowers of sulphur should be given. To do this, make a paper funnel, place a little powder in the bottom of the funnel, which is placed in the rabbit's ear. Blow into the funnel and the powder goes well down into the ear, and destroys any parasites that may be there.

Cannibalism in Does.—This is usually caused because the doe is short of fluid, or because the nest has been moved for some reason. Does get very thirsty at kindling time, and thirst, allied to the distress of kindling, makes them eat or mutilate their young. If a doe has eaten a previous litter or mutilated them, about three days before she is due to kindle, give her a dose of Linseed Oil, and oil of aniseed, mixed in the proportion of one part of aniseed to four parts of linseed. Linseed oil gently relaxes the muscular system, and oil of aniseed has a soothing effect on the nerves. A kindling doe should also have a liberal supply of water at all times.

Chill.—Young rabbits are liable to chills if they are not provided with plenty of bedding. While the youngsters are in the hutch with the doe, she should have plenty of bedding so that if the weather gets suddenly colder, she can put more bedding material on the nest. A nest box helps to prevent chills.

Coccidiosis.—Coccidiosis is one of the few serious diseases from which rabbits suffer, and one which causes more deaths among young rabbits than any other. There are two types of coccidiosis, one which affects the liver and one which affects the intestines. The disease is caused by a microscopic parasite, known as an oocyst. Probably the greatest source of infection for young rabbits is the doe. Many does suffer from this disease in a very mild form, and while they show no ill-effects, they can pass on the disease to the youngsters through the droppings. The disease can only be avoided if the young rabbits can be prevented from swallowing the infective oocysts. Almost daily cleaning out while the youngsters are with the doe is helpful, and all food should be fed from racks and bowls so that it does not come into contact with the hutch floor. A good diet also helps to raise resistance to the disease, particularly a few drops of cod liver oil added to the mash during cold and sunless weather. The symptoms of coccidiosis are that the rabbit sits huddled up, has a dry 'staring' coat, and begins to lose weight. The appetite may or may not be poor, but poor condition and failure to gain weight among young rabbits is one of the signs of coccidiosis. Coccidiosis is infectious, so litter from hutches which have housed infected animals should be burnt, If possible, go over the inside of the hutch with a painter's blow-lamp, then scrub well with a strong solution of household ammonia.

There is so far no known effective cure for coccidiosis. The remedy lies rather in prevention.

Colds.— Frequent sneezing and a discharge from the nose may mean nothing worse than a cold, but any rabbit with these symptoms should be isolated in case it has snuffles, which is much more serious. To cure a cold, give a daily injection in each nostril of an equal mixture camphorated and eucalyptus oils. If the cold does not yield to treatment in a few days snuffles should be suspected.

Conjunctivitis.—Inflammation of the eye, such as is sometimes encountered in bucks, is best treated by lotions, such as 10 per cent. Neoprotosil, or 10 per cent. Argyrol. These drops should be applied to the affected parts three or four times daily.

Constipation.—Constipation, the passing of few and dried up pellets, can usually be cured by giving increased amounts of greenfood, or by giving a half teaspoonful of medicinal paraffin.

Cysts.—There are two types of worm cysts in rabbits, one found in the liver, and the other under the skin or between the muscles. These are caused by the rabbits eating greenfood which has been fouled by dogs suffering from tape worm infection. The infection of the liver by these cysts often proves fatal, particularly to young rabbits, but the cysts which appear below the skin do no damage unless they are in a vital spot. These can be removed by a veterinary surgeon if the rabbit is a valuable one.

There is no cure for the liver infestation by tape worm, and the remedy in both cases lies rather in prevention than cure. Try to avoid greenfood which has been contaminated by dog droppings, and if any greenfood is suspect, immerse it in salt and water and leave to dry for twelve hours before feeding.

Diarrhoea or scours.—Diarrhoea is the condition in which the excreta is fluid or semi-fluid. It may be caused either by wrong feeding, or by the inflammation of the caecum, and it may be a symptom of disease. If the rabbit is eating, discontinue greenfood, except astringent greens like shepherds purse, strawberry or raspberry leaves. In severe cases give as much bismuth as can be placed on a threepenny bit every four hours, or else a drop of chlorodyne in a little warm milk.

Drooping ears.—These may be caused either by a hutch which is too low, or by careless handling or may be an inherited defect. If the cartilage is not seriously damaged the ear will usually return to normal.

External parasites.—Rabbits sometimes become infested with fleas and lice. These not only cause acute irritation, but spoil the condition of the pelt and lower the health of the rabbit. They can be dealt with by using D.D.T. or derris powder.

Eyes.—If eyes become damaged or eyelids torn as a result of fighting, it is better to consult a veterinary surgeon. For inflammation of the eye due to foreign bodies in the eye, or to colds, use lotions such as 10 per cent. Neoprotosil or 10 per cent. Argyrol.

Heat stroke.—In very hot weather, rabbits are liable to heat stroke if kept shut up in small badly ventilated hutches, or in travelling boxes. They should be put in a cool shady place, and given plenty of water to drink, and some hay and good greenfood.

Mastitis.—Does sometimes suffer with swollen milk glands after kindling, and owing to tenderness and the swelling they find it difficult to feed their young. The swollen parts should be fomented with hot water to which a little hydrogen peroxide has been added. Do this three or four times daily, and gently massage the glands with castor oil once a day. Do not give the doe much water to drink while the glands are swollen, but she should have plenty of good greenfood.

Mange.—This is caused by a small parasite. Scabs appear on the face, ears and lips, and the skin is bare, itchy and wrinkled. There are dry crusts and spots with a discharge of serum. Organic sulphur lotions can be used or a modern preparation such as Tetmosol.

Over-long nails.—Sometimes rabbits' nails grow so long that they begin to curl. Over-long nails are a nuisance to the rabbits, and can be dangerous in a doe if there are youngsters in the nest. The nails can be clipped quite easily with a pair of sharp pliers or wire cutters. Cut only the whitish, dried up part of the nail, and clip a little at a time. The 'live' part of the nail should never be cut.

Paralysis.—Usually attacks the hind-quarters, and is very difficult to cure. May be caused by damp or draughty hutches, or may be an inherited defect. Does rearing a large litter are sometimes attacked by paralysis. The rabbit should be kept in a warm hutch, and given three drops of syrup of hypophosphites in a teaspoonful of water twice a day until cured. If the rabbit does not show signs of recovery in a reasonable time it is better to destroy it.

Pica.—This is the eating of filth by rabbits. It must not be mistaken for coprophagy, when the animals take the specially formed pellets direct from the anus. This is normal, but the picking up of pellets from the floor is not. Pica is sometimes caused by a lack of fluid in the diet, or by diet deficiencies, and these should be remedied.

Red Water.—Generally due to cold or damp affecting the kidneys, but may also be caused by improper feeding, such as feeding too many greenfoods which are diuretic, that is, which have a marked effect on the kidneys. The urine passed is reddish coloured. The rabbit should be kept in a warm hutch, and given warm mash and barley water to drink. If this does not effect a cure, give two drops of sweet spirit of nitre in water, daily for three days.

Rickets.—Rickets is not common among tame rabbits, but it will affect youngsters if they suffer from deficiency in sunshine, greenfood or lime, or if the diet does not contain enough of vitamins A and D. If a rabbit has a good supply of greenfood, this supplies the necessary vitamins and minerals. If leg weakness does appear, give cod liver oil or halibut liver oil in the mash. Two or three drops are sufficient. It is a wise precaution to give such fish oil to does and youngsters during winter months. In summer the best treatment is to pen the youngsters outside in the sunshine, and to give them plenty of good greenfood.

Ringworm.—Very occasionally a rabbit is affected with ringworm. This shows itself in the form of red spots, which later form a yellow crust. These crusts fall off leaving small ulcers and scars. Ringworm should be treated with tincture of iodine or golden eye ointment. Strict attention should be paid to cleansing the hands and burning all dressings used, as ringworm can spread to human beings.

Scurf.—When rabbits have patches of scurf they should be treated with sulphur lotion and the animals should be given plenty of fresh greenfood, and water to drink. The mash meal, or cereal foods which are inclined to be heating, should be reduced, and extra greenfood given instead to get the blood into good condition.

Snuffles.—Snuffles is characterised by a thick yellowish discharge from the nose, and by persistent sneezing, this disease is quickly spread to other rabbits, and any animal that sneezes or has a discharge from the nose should be isolated at once. If the sneezing and discharge do not clear up in a few days, it is safer to destroy the affected animal before the trouble is spread, as snuffles is almost impossible to cure.

Sore Hocks.—This is a common trouble with Rex rabbits, owing to the short soft nature of their fur. It can be an inherited defect and for this reason it is unwise to breed from Rex rabbits which are prone to sore hocks. Overcrowding should be avoided, and the rabbits should always have plenty of clean dry bedding. A good thick layer of bedding is necessary for rabbits which have sore hocks. The affected parts can be treated with 1 : 1,000 acriflavine cream or other good antiseptic ointment. For white coated rabbits use 1: 5,000 perchloride of mercury.

Sterility.—Does are sometimes sterile, either they refuse to mate or if mated they produce no young. This is frequently due to the doe being overfat. The reproductive organs are the first to lay on fat, and in this condition they do not function as they should and so the doe becomes sterile. If the concentrated food is reduced, and hay and plenty of greenfood given instead so that the doe loses her excess fat, she will be much more likely to produce a litter.

Tuberculosis.—This is not a common disease among rabbits, but cases do occur at times. It can be brought about by giving rabbits milk from cows which are affected by T.B. (pasteurised milk will not cause infection.). Animals which lose weight and become unthrifty for no apparent reason may be suffering from this disease, and it is safer to destroy them.

Teeth (Overgrown).—Rabbits' front teeth grow from persistent pulps, that is they continue to grow throughout the animals' life. They are usually prevented from overgrowing by the fact that they impinge on each other. If for any reason the teeth become overgrown, causing the rabbit pain and making eating difficult, they can be filed down.

Twisted Neck Disease.—This is not so much a disease in itself, as a symptom of some other disease. The rabbit holds its head very much awry, and in some cases it cannot stand or move about. In some cases it is due to an infection of the ear, or spine, but frequently a careful post mortem fails to reveal any cause. There is no specific cure for this disease. Sometimes the rabbit recovers, but usually it is better to destroy it.

Vent Disease.—Vent disease or rabbit syphilis is spread during mating. It appears as small sores or scaly patches on or about the reproductive organs. All breeding animals should be carefully examined before being used for mating. The parts should be thoroughly cleansed and then a three per cent. solution of zinc acetate should be applied, or mercurial ointment in a thin layer. This treatment should continue daily until all signs of the disease have disappeared. Adult rabbits should have a regular examination about once a month to make sure that there are no signs of vent disease.

Worms.—Small round worms are very occasionally found among the excreta of rabbits. When the rabbit has been without food for several hours, preferably in the morning before the first feed, give as much grated areca nut as will lie on a one pence piece. Do this twice a week until all signs of worms have gone from the droppings.

To Dose a Rabbit.—If it is not possible to give any necessary medicine or powder in the rabbit's food, this is the best method of administering a dose. Get someone to hold the rabbit gently but firmly. Then insert the handle of a small teaspoon, in a flat position, into the side of the rabbit's mouth. Carefully turn the spoon handle so that the rabbit is forced to open its mouth. The powder or medicine can then be poured on to the rabbit's tongue from another spoon, and the spoon handle removed. Hold the rabbit's mouth gently until the medicine has been swallowed.

CHAPTER 13

EXHIBITING

EXHIBITING rabbits is an art, which, like all other arts, is best learnt by practice. The best way to learn the points of any breed of rabbit is to go to shows and watch the judging of that particular breed. This will help the novice more than anything else to recognise a good rabbit when he sees one. It will also help him to get an idea of the condition in which a rabbit should be sent to a show.

Newcomers to rabbit breeding sometimes imagine that there is some special way of getting a rabbit into show condition. If there is, then the secret lies in the feeding bowl and in general management. A rabbit that has not been well fed cannot be rushed into show condition in a week by giving it a little extra attention and grooming. One of the first essentials of a show rabbit is good health. Nothing else will give that bloom to the coat, and the vigour and alertness which are characteristic of the prize winning rabbit.

Show rabbits should be fed well on mash, good quality hay, and greenstuff or roots which are fresh and clean. Over feeding can be as detrimental as underfeeding, because an overfed rabbit will go off its food, and lose condition in this way. Rabbits really need to grow up in exhibition condition if they are to do really well, and it is a waste of time and money to show rabbits which are in poor condition.

A show rabbit should be handled daily, particularly as the show time approaches. Lift it out of the hutch, and sit it on a table or a box and groom with a soft brush, or with the hands. This has the double advantage of getting the rabbit used to being handled, and also of removing any loose hairs and giving the coat a nice gloss. Frequent handling helps the rabbit to overcome fright and shyness on the judging table. A rabbit which sits quietly and well, shows off its good points better than one which kicks and scratches or flattens itself in a position of terror.

Some rabbits are naturally quiet and placid when handled, others need a good deal of time and patience spent on them before they handle really well. You cannot make a bad rabbit into a good one, however well fed and well groomed it may be, but a moderate rabbit can be much improved by good feeding and grooming, and by being trained to sit quietly when handled.

A rabbit will not stand much chance at a show if it is in heavy moult, particularly if it is a fur rabbit. Slight moult may be overlooked if the rabbit is a particularly good one, but as a general rule, it is better to keep moulting rabbits at home. It is disappointing when one's best rabbit begins to moult just before a show, but there are always other shows to which it can be sent later on.

As a final preparation for a few days before showing, finish off the hand grooming by giving the rabbit a 'polish' with a piece of soft material, such as silk or a chamois leather.

Make your entries for the show in good time and plan the travelling arrangements so that your exhibits arrive in good time. Nothing complicates matters so much for the secretary and stewards of a show as rabbits which arrive late, and there is always a risk that the late arrival may miss the judging of its particular class.

Good travelling boxes are most important. Show rabbits may have to spend quite a long time in their travelling boxes, and it is essential that they should be comfortable. Cramped boxes, which allow the animal no room to move, cause them much discomfort, if not actual suffering, and mean that they will not look their best when they arrive. Boxes which are over-big are nearly as bad, because they allow the animal to be thrown about.

A good sized box for an average rabbit is eighteen inches long, twelve inches wide and fourteen inches deep. Good travelling boxes can be bought, but if they are made at home they should be of strong and solid construction. They have to stand up to a good deal of handling, both in transit and at the shows, and a flimsy box gives no real protection to the animal inside.

Put plenty of straw in the box for bedding, otherwise the rabbit may arrive at the show in a stained and dirty condition.

Put some hay in for the rabbit to eat, and a crust of bread. A piece of root such as a carrot can be put in also, but greenfood is not much good, it becomes trampled and soiled before it is eaten.

See that boxes are clearly labelled, both for their destination, and with the owner's name and address. A travelling box which arrives at a show with no indication as to where it came from, or where its occupant is to be returned, is a worry to the show stewards, and causes a lot of unnecessary work.

INDEX